D1095426

CHABOT COLLEGE-HAYWARD

2 555 000 002197 -

60746   D
                         764
Kluge   K5363

The battle

Date Due

MR 6'74		
JUN 10 '82		

CHABOT
COLLEGE
LIBRARY

25555 Hesperian Boulevard
Hayward, California 94545

 PRINTED IN U.S.A.

The Battle

Books by Alexander Kluge

Attendance List for a Funeral

The Battle

Alexander Kluge

The Battle

Translated from the German by Leila Vennewitz

McGraw-Hill Book Company

New York Toronto London Sydney

D
764
K5363

Translator's Acknowledgment

I am greatly indebted to Brigadier General S.L.A. Marshall, U.S.A.R., Rtd., of Birmingham, Michigan; and to my brother, Sir John Croot, C.B.E., F.R.C.S., of Kampala, Uganda, for their careful scrutiny of this translation and the helpful suggestions they have made based on their own expert technical knowledge. I wish also to express my deep appreciation for the continuing assistance and advice given me by my husband, William Vennewitz.

Leila Vennewitz

Vancouver, Canada

Copyright © 1967 by Alexander Kluge. All Rights Reserved. Printed in the United States of America. This book, or parts thereof, may not be reproduced in any form without permission of the publishers.
Library of Congress Catalog Card Number: 67-19149
35069   First Edition

Originally published under the title *Schlachtbeschreibung;* © 1964 by Walter-Verlag, Olten and Freiburg in Breisgau, Germany.

HUMBOT COLLEGE LIBRARY

HAYWARD, CALIFORNIA

Foreword

This book describes the organizational build-up of a disaster. The subject is the disaster of Stalingrad. The causes date back thirty days or three hundred years.

Alexander Kluge

60746

Contents

The future is also unfortunately

no longer what it was.

Paul Valéry

The Battle

Report

Tuesday, November 10, 1942
 In Stalingrad, patrol activity.

Wednesday, November 11, 1942
 In Stalingrad, strong patrol activity.

Thursday, November 12, 1942
 In Stalingrad patrols routed the enemy from additional city blocks and bases in fierce assault fighting. Army artillery and Luftwaffe antiaircraft sank five large troop ferries and freight barges on the Volga. Artillery positions and supply routes to the east of the river were heavily damaged by air attacks.

Friday, November 13, 1942
 In Stalingrad, scattered enemy groups were cleaned up in the territory gained the previous day.

Saturday, November 14, 1942
 South of Stalingrad, local Bolshevik attacks were repulsed by the defensive fire of Rumanian troops. In Stalingrad shock troops occupied further city blocks in fierce fighting. Enemy counterattacks were repulsed, and troop concentrations were destroyed by combined artillery and antiaircraft as well as dive bombers.

Sunday, November 15, 1942

In the city of Stalingrad enemy counterattacks were repulsed. The Luftwaffe gave effective support by attacking Soviet artillery positions and airfields to the east of the Volga.

Monday, November 16, 1942

In Stalingrad, further city blocks were occupied and enemy counterattacks repulsed by patrol activity.

Tuesday, November 17, 1942

Nothing.

Wednesday, November 18, 1942

Nothing.

Thursday, November 19, 1942

In Stalingrad, patrol clashes. Rumanian troops repulsed a number of attacks on the Don front, during which the Rumanian air force inflicted considerable losses on the enemy. A new battle is in progress here.

Friday, November 20, 1942

In Stalingrad our patrols occupied some city blocks. Enemy counterassaults collapsed. On the Don front Rumanian and German troops are engaged in fierce fighting against strong enemy tank and infantry attacks.

Saturday, November 21, 1942

South of Stalingrad and in the Kalmuck steppe, the enemy commenced an attack with strong forces supported by tanks in the course of which a motorized enemy unit was wiped out. On the lower Don, a fierce defensive battle on the part of German and Rumanian troops continues. A reinforced cavalry regiment that had broken through our positions was encircled and destroyed.

Sunday, November 22, 1942

In the area south of Stalingrad and in the big bend of the Don, the fierce defensive battle continues. In one counterattack German and Rumanian troops captured 600 prisoners and destroyed twenty-five tanks. On November 20 and 21 a further thirty-six Soviet tanks were destroyed by a Panzer division. The German and Rumanian air forces supported our troops and inflicted heavy losses on the enemy in waves of attacks against tank concentrations, infantry units, unloading points, and truck columns. In Stalingrad patrol action resulted in the further occupation of strongly fortified bases and elsewhere repulsed Soviet attacks.

Monday, November 23, 1942

In the area south of Stalingrad and in the big bend of the Don, German and Rumanian units, combined with powerful close-combat aerial units, continue to engage in heavy defensive fighting. In the central sector, during temporarily improved weather conditions, fighter planes and dive bombers were used to attack enemy artillery positions and troop quarters.

Tuesday, November 24, 1942

South of Stalingrad and in the big bend of the Don, the Soviets, with a complete disregard for their own men and equipment, penetrated the defense front on the Don. Countermeasures are now being taken. During the fierce and fluctuating fighting of the last two days, several hundred enemy tanks were destroyed. Despite unfavorable flying weather, the German and Rumanian air forces participated repeatedly in the fighting taking place on the ground. In Stalingrad itself, local fighting only.

Wednesday, November 25, 1942

Southwest of Stalingrad and in the big bend of the Don, the enemy continued to attack with strong infantry and armored forces. Our own defense was effectively and continuously supported by strong close-range aerial units as well as German and Rumanian fighter planes. Soviet troops again suffered heavy losses in men and matériel. Simultaneous attacks of the enemy between the Volga and the Don were repulsed by German and Rumanian troops in fierce fighting which resulted in heavy losses in men for the enemy, and fifty-four tanks were destroyed. In Stalingrad itself, enemy attacks also failed. Along the rest of the eastern front our own patrol actions were successful and enemy attacks were repulsed.

Thursday, November 26, 1942

Between the Volga and the Don and in the big bend of the Don, the heavy tank and infantry attacks of the enemy continue. They were repulsed in fierce fighting. The enemy again lost numerous tanks. Our air attacks inflicted heavy losses in men, heavy weapons, and vehicles of all kinds on the enemy. In Stalingrad, enemy assault attempts again collapsed yesterday.

Friday, November 27, 1942

All tank and infantry attacks of the enemy in the Volga–Don area failed again yesterday because of the excellent fighting spirit of our troops. Fifty-five Soviet tanks were destroyed. Attacks by dive-bomber units struck annihilating blows at the enemy. Army troops sank two motor vessels on the Volga near Stalingrad.

Saturday, November 28, 1942

Between the Volga and the Don, in the big bend of the Don and in Stalingrad, heavy enemy attacks were again repulsed in fierce fighting. Antiaircraft artillery and fighter planes participated effectively in the ground fighting and destroyed thirty-four Soviet tanks. According to reports to date, from November 20 to 27 the enemy lost 319 tanks between the Volga and the Don. In addition, twenty-six artillery pieces were destroyed and more than 2,000 prisoners taken.

Sunday, November 29, 1942

Yesterday German and Rumanian troops again repulsed all attacks of numerically superior enemy forces between the Volga and the Don, inflicting bloody losses. Thirty-five tanks were destroyed. In the big bend of the Don, a counterattack of our troops threw the Soviets back across a section of the river. Strong air units, including Rumanian fighter planes, successfully supported Army troops. A large number of vehicles were destroyed. Sections of the railway along the lower Volga were successfully bombed during the night. Fast Italian fighter planes attacked motorized enemy columns and troop quarters.

Monday, November 30, 1942

Between the Volga and the Don, Army units, in close cooperation with strong air units, repulsed renewed violent tank and infantry attacks. In Stalingrad, local fighting only.

Tuesday, December 1, 1942

Continued assault attempts on the part of the Soviets yesterday between the Volga and the Don were unsuccessful and resulted in exceptionally high enemy losses.

Wednesday, December 2, 1942

Fast Italian and heavy German fighter planes were used against strong enemy troop movements along the central Don.

Thursday, December 3, 1942

Renewed attacks on the part of strong enemy infantry and armored units were again unsuccessful yesterday in the Volga–Don area owing to the stubborn resistance of German and Rumanian troops.

Friday, December 4, 1942

During yesterday's continued fierce defensive battle between the Volga and the Don, repeated powerful attacks of the Soviets collapsed with heavy losses. Thirty-six tanks were destroyed. Hundreds of prisoners, weapons, and other matériel fell into the hands of our troops.

Saturday, December 5, 1942

On December 4 the Soviets initiated a further unsuccessful attack between the Volga and the Don, employing large numbers of tanks. Seventy-five were destroyed, thirteen were put out of action, and heavy losses in men and matériel were inflicted on the enemy. A powerful attack on the part of our Panzer troops destroyed enemy tank and cavalry forces, in the course of which 2,000 prisoners and fourteen artillery pieces were captured. Italian and Hungarian reconnaissance action along the Don front yielded important information.

Sunday, December 6, 1942

In fluctuating fighting between the Volga and the Don, a Soviet battalion was destroyed, twenty-six tanks were put out of action, and numerous artillery pieces and infantry weapons of the enemy were captured. Despite extremely unfavorable weather conditions, the transport units of the Luftwaffe maintained supplies to the fighting troops. In the successful defensive battle between the Volga and the Don, the 2nd Battalion of a Viennese grenadier regiment distinguished itself by its exemplary behavior. During the preceding few days, Soviet attacks, supported by tanks, were repeatedly repulsed on an important section of the river in the big bend of the Don.

Monday, December 7, 1942

North of the Terek, between the Volga and the Don, and in the big bend of the Don, the enemy, employing fresh forces, unsuccessfully assaulted the German–Rumanian positions.

Tuesday, December 8, 1942

Yesterday, in the big bend of the Don, the Soviets resumed their violent attacks and suffered heavy tank losses. The attacks were frustrated by the resistance of our troops, who were supported by German and Rumanian fighter planes.

Wednesday, December 9, 1942

Renewed Soviet attempts to penetrate the German positions in the eastern Caucasus and the Volga–Don area failed again yesterday with severe losses to the enemy. Mass enemy attacks on the part of infantry and armored units between the Volga and the Don led to severe fighting in which our troops were successful. Prisoners and equipment were captured. In a counterattack in the big bend of the Don, German Panzer grenadiers dislodged the enemy from his positions and put forty-six Soviet tanks out of action with no losses to our own tanks.

Thursday, December 10, 1942

Enemy forces that had succeeded in effecting a breakthrough were encircled and destroyed between the Volga and the Don. In continuing their unsuccessful attacks, the Soviets suffered renewed heavy losses. On the eighth and ninth of this month they lost 104 tanks in this sector alone. Despite heavy counterfire, infantry and Panzer troops threw the enemy still farther back in the big bend of the Don, repulsed counterattacks, and destroyed sixteen Soviet tanks.

Friday, December 11, 1942

In the southern sector of the eastern front, brisk fighting continued in the course of which minor enemy forces were destroyed in the area north of Stalingrad. In the Don bend a dominating ridge was taken in severe fighting. All enemy counterattacks failed. In a powerful reconnaissance action, Italian troops penetrated the enemy positions and brought back prisoners and equipment. Enemy reconnaissance sorties were repulsed by Hungarian troops. Strong German and Rumanian air force units participated in the action in the Volga–Don area. Fighter planes shot down twenty-four enemy aircraft. Combat and ground-strafing planes continued to harass enemy deployment along the central Don.

Saturday, December 12, 1942

In the southern sector of the eastern front, German, Italian, and Rumanian troops, supported by Luftwaffe units, repulsed repeated enemy attacks, inflicting losses on the enemy.

Sunday, December 13, 1942

Local Soviet attacks in the Volga–Don area failed against the resistance of German and Italian troops. On the east bank of the Don, Hungarian patrols destroyed enemy installations. Prisoners and equipment were captured.

Monday, December 14, 1942

Fighting, at times very severe, against a strong enemy continues in . . . parts of the southern sector of the front. Our Panzer forces, advancing from the area southwest of Stalingrad, destroyed strong enemy forces whose counterattacks failed and resulted in the loss of more than twenty tanks. In the course of an advance in the rear of the enemy carried out during the past few days in the Kalmuck steppe, a large number of prisoners were captured and enemy supplies seriously disrupted.

Tuesday, December 15, 1942

In the Volga–Don area, infantry and Panzer units repulsed enemy tank attacks in severe fighting. They inflicted heavy losses on the Soviets and destroyed sixty-seven tanks.

Wednesday, December 16, 1942

German and Rumanian troops captured various stubbornly defended villages between the Volga and the Don and repulsed counterattacks with severe losses to the enemy.

Thursday, December 17, 1942

German and Rumanian troops, supported by combat planes, attacked and beat back the enemy between the Volga and the Don; in the big bend of the Don they repulsed repeated attacks by strong forces, sometimes by counterattacks. Thirty Soviet tanks were destroyed.

Friday, December 18, 1942

Enemy attacks in the area of the Terek, Stalingrad, and the big bend of the Don were unsuccessful and met with heavy losses. More than twenty tanks were destroyed. Between the Volga and the Don, German divisions broke through strongly fortified enemy positions on a dominating ridge and gained new territory in their attack.

9

Saturday, December 19, 1942

Despite stubborn resistance, German and Rumanian troops forced back the enemy between the Volga and the Don farther toward the northeast. In their counterattacks the Soviets lost twenty-two tanks. In Stalingrad and the big bend of the Don, enemy attacks were repulsed.

Sunday, December 20, 1942

Between the Volga and the Don, German Panzer divisions, in cooperation with Rumanian troops, attacked the stubbornly resisting enemy and gained an important sector of the river. Strong enemy attacks in the area of Stalingrad and the big bend of the Don were repulsed in bitter fighting, in some cases with counterattacks. In the course of this fighting the Soviets lost 164 tanks.

Monday, December 21, 1942

In the Volga–Don area heavy fighting continues. In fierce Panzer and infantry battles the Soviets again suffered extremely heavy losses in men and equipment. According to incomplete reports, more than seventy enemy tanks were destroyed yesterday in the Don sector. Along the central Don the enemy, who had been attacking for days with an extremely heavy concentration of armored units, succeeded in effecting a breakthrough in the defense front there. This breakthrough cost the Bolsheviks enormous losses. In order to counter a threat to their flanks, the approaching German divisions occupied planned positions to the rear, thus containing the successful enemy attacks.

Tuesday, December 22, 1942

In Stalingrad the enemy attempted to gain a foothold by attacking across the Volga. The enemy was repulsed in bitter hand-to-hand fighting. The defense battle along the central Don continues with unabated violence.

Wednesday, December 23, 1942

In the course of renewed unsuccessful attacks between the Volga and the Don and in Stalingrad, the Soviets suffered heavy losses. Along the central Don the heavy fighting continues.

Thursday, December 24, 1942

In the Kalmuck steppe, German troops repulsed repeated enemy attacks and inflicted bloody losses on the enemy in a successful assault. A Soviet cavalry unit appearing in the rear was attacked and routed in the subsequent pursuit. During the attack between the Volga and the Don, 600 prisoners were captured and fifteen tanks destroyed. Soviet counterattacks collapsed. In the Don area the defensive battle continues in fluctuating fighting.

Friday, December 25, 1942

In the course of the previous day, our heroically fighting troops, supported by newly arrived units, went over to counterattack at several points in the Don area. In bitter fighting they destroyed enemy motorized and tank units that were trying to penetrate to the rear of our troops through gaps in the newly formed front.

Saturday, December 26, 1942

Between the Volga and the Don and in the Don area, continuing enemy attacks were repulsed by the stubborn resistance of our troops. German troops forced back the Soviets in counterattacks at several points. Forty-two tanks were put out of action. Strong Luftwaffe units and fast Hungarian fighter planes supported the Army by day and by night.

Sunday, December 27, 1942

Enemy attacks between the Volga and the Don and in the Stalingrad area were repulsed.

Monday, December 28, 1942

In the course of yesterday's successful defensive fighting between the Volga and the Don and in the big bend of the Don, ninety-five Soviet tanks were destroyed.

Tuesday, December 29, 1942

Between the Volga and the Don and in the big bend of the Don, renewed enemy attacks failed against stubborn resistance. An enemy unit that had been encircled for some days was wiped out. Since December 24, with the support of the Luftwaffe, sixty-five tanks, thirty heavy guns, numerous heavy and light infantry weapons, and other war matériel were destroyed or captured and a large number of prisoners brought in. The bloody losses of the enemy exceeded these numbers many times. During the defensive battle in the big bend of the Don, the Italian division Julia distinguished itself especially.

Wednesday, December 30, 1942

In Stalingrad and the Don area, the Soviets suffered heavy losses during their continued attacks and lost sixteen tanks. In the course of successful counterattacks, large numbers of heavy and light weapons and prisoners were captured. Attacks by German air squadrons as well as Italian, Rumanian, and Hungarian combat planes inflicted heavy losses on the enemy and serious damage to tanks and heavy weapons. Hungarian patrols destroyed a large number of enemy pillboxes and their crews.

Thursday, December 31, 1942

In the Don area, enemy attacks were repulsed in severe fighting. The Soviets suffered heavy losses and again lost large numbers of tanks. The German counterattack gained further territory.

Friday, January 1, 1943

In the Terek area, Stalingrad, and the big bend of the Don, the enemy again suffered heavy losses in continuing its unsuccessful attacks and lost thirty-three tanks.

Saturday, January 2, 1943

Renewed attacks of the enemy were again unsuccessful in heavy fighting in the Don area. Successful counterattacks on the part of German troops repulsed the enemy and wiped out an enemy tank brigade, destroying thirty-nine tanks and fourteen artillery pieces in the process.

Sunday, January 3, 1943

Heavy defensive fighting continues in the Don area. The enemy was beaten back along the entire front and lost thirty-eight tanks. During this fighting, the 6th Panzer Division distinguished itself especially. Hungarian troops repulsed a Soviet attack that was supported by strong artillery.

Monday, January 4, 1943

In various sectors of the front in the Don area and in the Stalingrad area, the Soviets suffered heavy losses in continuing their attacks.

Tuesday, January 5, 1943

Heavy defense fighting in the Don area continues.

Wednesday, January 6, 1943

Yesterday the heavy defense fighting in the Don area continued with undiminished intensity. Soviet attacks were beaten back with heavy losses to the enemy. One Panzer division put thirty-one tanks out of action.

Thursday, January 7, 1943

The fighting in the Don and Kalmuck area and in the Stalingrad area continues. In the course of this fighting, German infantry and Panzer divisions, in cooperation with strong Luftwaffe units and Rumanian fighter planes, repulsed all Soviet attacks. In a counterattack, twenty enemy tanks were destroyed at one point.

Friday, January 8, 1943

Yesterday in the area of the . . . Don and northwest of Stalingrad, German troops were again engaged in heavy but successful defense battles with strong Soviet infantry and tank forces. In a counterattack the enemy was thrown back at various points and suffered heavy losses. Thirty-two tanks were destroyed.

Saturday, January 9, 1943

Heavy fighting continues between the Caucasus and the Don, near Stalingrad, and in the Don area. The grimly attacking Soviets were beaten back everywhere. The German troops, counterattacking immediately at many points, inflicted severe and bloody losses on the enemy and destroyed large quantities of war equipment.

Sunday, January 10, 1943

In Stalingrad, local patrols active. Fighter planes shot down twelve Soviet planes with no losses to themselves.

Monday, January 11, 1943

In northern Caucasia, near Stalingrad, and in the Don area, continued attacks of numerically superior Soviet infantry and tank forces were repulsed in severe fighting. The German Luftwaffe participated in the action with strong forces. In a counterattack, infantry and Panzer troops destroyed enemy units. Army and Luftwaffe destroyed or put out of action 136 tanks, 60 in the Stalingrad area alone.

Tuesday, January 12, 1943

In the Stalingrad as well as Don areas, the enemy, again employing strong forces, continued to attack focal points. The enemy was repulsed in fierce fighting, sometimes in counterattack, and lost sixty-three tanks, forty-five near Stalingrad alone. Soviet losses correspond to the mass employment of infantry.

Wednesday, January 13, 1943

Nothing.

Thursday, January 14, 1943

In the Stalingrad area, German troops repulsed strong infantry and armored attacks in fierce, heroic fighting.

Friday, January 15, 1943

In the Stalingrad area, German troops defended themselves in bitter fighting against continuing heavy attacks by the enemy. Seventy-five Soviet tanks were destroyed, thirty-five of them near Stalingrad.

Saturday, January 16, 1943

In the Stalingrad area our troops, which have been engaged for weeks in a heroic and courageous defensive battle against the enemy who has been attacking from all sides, yesterday again repulsed heavy attacks of enemy infantry and Panzer units, inflicting serious losses on the Bolsheviks. Officers and men again offered a shining example of the heroic German soldier spirit.

Sunday, January 17, 1943

In the Stalingrad area our troops continued to engage in heavy defense fighting against renewed mass attacks on the part of the enemy, attacks which were frustrated by the determined resistance of the courageous defenders.

Monday, January 18, 1943

German troops in the Stalingrad area fighting under the most difficult conditions resisted further strong attacks with stubborn endurance and a defiant fighting spirit.

Tuesday, January 19, 1943

The troops in the Stalingrad area defended themselves valiantly in severe fighting against repeated new enemy attacks.

Wednesday, January 20, 1943

The defenders of the Stalingrad area steadily repulsed all Soviet attacks in spite of severe privations.

Thursday, January 21, 1943

The German troops in the Stalingrad area continued to offer the utmost resistance to the unceasing efforts of the enemy to penetrate the defense front, and repulsed mass attacks in fierce fighting.

Friday, January 22, 1943

The German forces in Stalingrad, tightly encircled by the enemy and offering stubborn resistance to strong enemy pressure, were subjected again yesterday to heavy fighting against the far superior forces of attacking Soviets. Despite heroic resistance, the defenders of Stalingrad could not prevent a breakthrough from the west, making it necessary to take back their own positions by some miles.

Saturday, January 23, 1943

Throughout the whole of yesterday, the defenders of Stalingrad grappled heroically with the far superior enemy. Twenty tanks were destroyed in close combat. A deep enemy penetration in the defense front was intercepted by straining every effort. Heavy defense battles along the central Don and south of Lake Ladoga continue.

Sunday, January 24, 1943

The situation near Stalingrad has become more acute because of the further breakthrough of strong enemy masses from the west. Nevertheless, the defenders continue as a shining example of the best German soldier spirit to hold the steadily narrowing circle around the city. With their heroic efforts they are tying up strong enemy forces and for many months have been cutting off enemy supply routes at one of their most important points.

Monday, January 25, 1943

In Stalingrad the 6th Army is pinning immortal glory to its banners in its heroic and self-sacrificing battle against overwhelming odds. Units of the Rumanian 20th Infantry Division and the 1st Cavalry Division are fighting shoulder to shoulder with their German comrades to the last and share to the fullest extent in this glory.

Tuesday, January 26, 1943

In Stalingrad the defenders, including as well as the Rumanian divisions a small Croatian detachment, have concentrated in a small area in the southern and central part of the city ruins. There, led by their generals, they continue to offer heroic resistance, supported to the utmost by the Luftwaffe under the most difficult conditions.

Wednesday, January 27, 1943

Those sections of the 6th Army still able to fight are clinging with might and main to the ruins of the city of Stalingrad. While making use of every possibility of defense against ceaseless Soviet attacks on the ground and in the air, they are tying up the forces of several Soviet armies. An enemy detachment that had penetrated the city was repulsed in fierce fighting.

Thursday, January 28, 1943

In Stalingrad the heroic resistance of the defenders remains unbroken. Soviet assaults on the west and south fronts collapsed with heavy losses to the enemy.

Friday, January 29, 1943

In Stalingrad furious enemy attacks on the south front are in progress and continue to be defied by the defenders despite the severest privations and overwhelming superiority of the enemy.

Saturday, January 30, 1943

In Stalingrad the situation is unchanged. The courage of the defenders is unbroken.

Sunday, January 31, 1943

In Stalingrad the enemy began approaching from all sides toward the defense positions and is now attacking concentrically. The southern forces, fighting heroically under the personal command of Field Marshal General Paulus, have been compressed into the narrowest possible area and are offering their final resistance in the building of the GPU. In the northern section of the city, under the command of the XI Army Corps, the defenders repulsed the attacks of the enemy on the west façade of the tractor plant.

Monday, February 1, 1943

In Stalingrad the southern group of the 6th Army, under the command of Field Marshal General Paulus, has been overcome by the superiority of the enemy after more than two months of heroic defense. The northern group, under the command of General of the Infantry Strecker, is still carrying on its defense. It is repulsing strong enemy attacks, sometimes with counterattacks. At the remaining focal points of the great defense battle in the east, fighting continues with undiminished violence.

Tuesday, February 2, 1943

In Stalingrad the enemy commenced the attack on the last bastion of the defenders, the tractor plant, after powerful artillery preparation with far superior forces. During the night, after our heroically fighting troops had used up almost all their ammunition, the enemy succeeded in penetrating at several points and in breaking the defense ring of the XI Army Corps which until then had remained intact.

Wednesday, February 3, 1943

The battle of Stalingrad is over. Loyal to their oath till the last breath, the 6th Army, under the exemplary command of Field Marshal General Paulus, has succumbed to the superiority of the enemy and the unfavorable conditions. Its fate is shared by an antiaircraft division of the German Luftwaffe, two Rumanian divisions, and a Croatian regiment, which have done their duty to the utmost in loyal comradeship with their fellow soldiers of the German Army. The time has not yet come to describe the course of the operations leading to these events. But one thing can already be said: the sacrifice of the Army was not in vain. For many weeks, as the bulwark of the historic European mission, it broke the assault of six Soviet armies. Throughout still more weeks of the severest fighting and utmost privation, totally encircled by the enemy, it kept strong enemy forces tied up. In this way it gave the German command the time and the opportunity to effect countermeasures on which the fate of the entire eastern front depended. Faced with this task, the 6th Army finally held on until, as encirclement progressed and the operation continued, the Luftwaffe was no longer in a position, despite extreme efforts and severe losses, to ensure adequate supplies from the air, and the possibility of relief increasingly and, finally, entirely disappeared. The surrender twice demanded by the enemy met with proud rejection. Under the swastika banner, hoisted on the highest ruin of Stalingrad and visible over a wide expanse, the final battle was fought. Generals, officers, noncommissioned officers, and men fought shoulder to shoulder to the last cartridge. They died that Germany might live. Their example will echo down the ages despite all the Bolsheviks' lying propaganda. Meanwhile the divisions of the 6th Army are already in process of being re-created.

Press reaction

Monday, November 23, 1942

V.I. No. 302/42

I. Reich Press Chief's Order of the Day:

    1. ... etc.

II. For information only:

  (a) Newspapers are advised that under no circumstances is the *heavy defensive fighting in the Stalingrad area* reported in today's Supreme Command communiqué to be referred to in headlines.

  (b) Franco's birthday. . . .

  (c) Foreign reports referring to letters from German prisoners of war in Russia are not to be published by the newspapers until a directive has been received.

Tuesday, November 24, 1942

V.I. No. 303/42

I. Reich Press Chief's Order of the Day:

    1. ... Anti-Comintern Pact. . . .

    2. Until the outcome of operations has been clarified, comments on the situation in the *area south of Stalingrad* and in the *big bend of the Don* are to be restricted to emphasis on the severity of the defensive battle.

II. For information only:

  (a) The heavy defensive fighting in the east referred to in the Supreme Command communiqué is not to be stressed in the press but may be given two-column headlines.

  (b) For several reasons the press is reminded not to report on *the new winter uniforms for our soldiers on the eastern front*. The article in the magazine *Our Army*, November 24 issue, concerning the new winter equipment, is likewise not to be reprinted.

Wednesday, November 25, 1942

V.I. No. 304/42

I. Reich Press Chief's Order of the Day:

    1. . . .

    2. The severity of the *fighting in the Stalingrad area* is to be emphasized with two-column headlines in line with the wording of the Supreme Command communiqué.

II. For information only:

    (a) . . .

III. Further comments on the Order of the Day:

    1. . . .

    2. As recommended to the press yesterday, the heavy defensive fighting near Stalingrad and in the big bend of the Don is to be published again today on the front page with two-column headlines in keeping with the Supreme Command communiqué. Needless to say, this item is not to form the focal point of the front-page make-up.

Thursday, November 26, 1942

V.I. No. 305/42

I. Reich Press Chief's Order of the Day:

    1. The severity of the fighting in the east is to be emphasized as before with two-column headlines.

    2. . . .

Saturday, November 28, 1942

V.I. No. 307/42

I. Reich Press Chief's Order of the Day:

    1. The heavy *defensive fighting in the central sector* of the eastern front is to be reported with two-column headlines.

Monday, November 30, 1942
V.I. No. 308/42
I. Reich Press Chief's Order of the Day:
  1. Reporting *on the heavy defensive fighting in the east* is to continue along the same lines.

Saturday, December 5, 1942
V.I. No. 313/42
I. Reich Press Chief's Order of the Day:
  1. The main feature of the military situation in the east is the remarkable successes obtained in heavy defensive battles. However, there is to be no change in the restrained treatment of the situation in all war theaters.

Tuesday, December 8, 1942
V.I. No. 315/42
I. Reich Press Chief's Order of the Day:
  1. . . .
  2. . . .
  3. The expected mention of the *contribution made by the Luftwaffe transport units* on the eastern front and in the Mediterranean area in the Supreme Command communiqué merits particular emphasis.

Wednesday, December 9, 1942
V.I. No. 316/42
I. Reich Press Chief's Order of the Day:
  1. . . .
  2. The *successful attacks in the central sector of the eastern front* announced in the Supreme Command communiqué merit particular emphasis.
II. . . .

III. Further comments on the Order of the Day:
   1. . . . .
   2. Newspapers are advised that the term "emphasis" does not imply a big spread: it is sufficient to report the successful attacks in the central sector of the eastern front, announced in the Supreme Command communiqué, on the front page with two-column headlines.

Friday, December 11, 1942
V.I. No. 318/42
I. Reich Press Chief's Order of the Day:
   1. . . . .
   2. The defensive successes on the eastern front, leading to the surrounding of an enemy force in the central sector and the destruction of 1,662 Soviet tanks, merit emphasis.

Monday, December 21, 1942
V.I. No. 327/42
I. Reich Press Chief's Order of the Day:
   3. While the *fighting on the central eastern front* has proved an unequivocal success on the part of the German defense, the severity of the battle on the Don front merits emphasis in keeping with the wording of the Supreme Command communiqué.

Tuesday, December 22, 1942
V.I. No. 328/42
I. Reich Press Chief's Order of the Day:
   1. . . . .
   2. The continuing severity of the defensive battle in the Volga–Don area is to be stressed in keeping with the Supreme Command communiqué. The heavy Bolshevik losses, particularly of tanks, are to be prominently reported with

continued stress on the cooperation of allied Rumanian and Italian troops.

(For the next two weeks there is no mention of Stalingrad either directly or indirectly.)

Tuesday, January 5, 1943
V.I. No. 5/43
I. Reich Press Chief's Order of the Day:
   1. The severity of the defensive battles on the various sectors of the eastern front now warrants greater prominence again.

Friday, January 8, 1943
V.I. No. 8/43
   Further comments on the Order of the Day:
   (a) The winter equipment of the Army in the east can now be referred to in the press but is not to form the subject of special articles or editorials.

Thursday, January 14, 1943
V.I. No. 13/43
I. Reich Press Chief's Order of the Day:
   1. . . .
   6. In death announcements of those killed in action, only such place names may be mentioned as have been named in Army communiqués. Otherwise, only general areas are to be given.

Friday, January 15, 1943
V.I. No. 14/43
I. Reich Press Chief's Order of the Day:
   1. *Over-all military reporting* will continue to deal mainly with

60746

extremely heavy defensive battles at numerous points along the eastern front.

2. . . .

Saturday, January 16, 1943
V.I. No. 15/43
I. Reich Press Chief's Order of the Day:
    1. . . . etc.
II. Addendum to the Order of the Day:
    5. Corresponding to the wording of the Supreme Command communiqué, the determined and severe *defensive battle of the German barrier position in the Stalingrad area* is to be emphasized in headlines and general positioning.

Monday, January 18, 1943
V.I. No. 17/43
I. Reich Press Chief's Order of the Day:
    1. The *severity of the battles on all sectors of the eastern front,* as well as the *heroic struggle of our troops in the Stalingrad area,* will be most prominently featured in the papers.
    2. . . .

Tuesday, January 19, 1943
V.I. No. 18/43
I. Reich Press Chief's Order of the Day:
    1. Now that the severity of the *winter battle in the east* has been brought home to the public by news reporting, increased personal efforts must be made by editors to rouse their readers to a supreme determination and spirit of self-sacrifice as displayed by the soldiers in the east.

Friday, January 22, 1943
V.I. No. 21/43
I. Reich Press Chief's Order of the Day:
1. *In consideration of the serious battles in the east* and the necessary determined increase in readiness to serve on the home front, an appeal is to be made to readers in this Sunday's edition, and it must be borne in on them with all urgency that the war requires the utmost willingness to serve on the part of all in order to achieve victory.
II. For information only:
(a) . . . etc.
(b) Make regular use of such propaganda phrases as:
   "Victory or Bolshevism!"
   "Total war means the mobilization of the whole nation!"
   "Only iron determination masters fate!"
   "Total war—all efforts for victory!"

Saturday, January 23, 1943
V.I. No. 21/43 (supplement)
I. Reich Press Chief's Order of the Day:
1. The supreme and gripping heroic sacrifice being made for the German nation by the *German troops surrounded at Stalingrad*, combined with the imminent compulsory labor for women and other far-reaching organizational measures for total warfare, will become the moral stimulus to a truly heroic attitude of the entire German people, as well as the commencement of a new chapter in the German will to victory and the summoning of all available forces. To the German press falls the special task of publishing such gripping descriptions of the unique spirit of self-sacrifice on the part of the heroes of Stalingrad that every last German fellow citizen will be roused to enter the great ranks of determined resistance and will to victory. Editors are requested to prepare for this mood of solemnity, which will

27

also encompass the celebrations of January 30, in order to ensure the necessary complete effectiveness of the anticipated appeals and announcements.

The editorials in the Sunday editions are to express the idea that the thoughts of the entire German nation are with its heroic fighters in Stalingrad.

Further comments on Point 1:
With the exception of the last sentence, Point 1 of the Order of the Day is for information only. Hence all mention of compulsory labor for women and other organizational measures is expressly prohibited until an official announcement has been made.

Sunday, January 24, 1943
V.I. No. 22/43
I. Reich Press Chief's Order of the Day:
    1. . . .
II. For information only:
    (a) . . . etc.
    (b) The *heroic epic of Stalingrad* will continue to be given due prominence.

Date illegible:
V.I. No. 24/43
I. Reich Press Chief's Order of the Day:
    1. The *heroic battle in Stalingrad* will continue to be given front-page prominence in the newspapers.

Wednesday, January 27, 1943
V.I. No. 25/43
I. Reich Press Chief's Order of the Day:
    1. The image of the German press will continue to be defined

by the gravity of the fighting in the east, but also by the confidence, arising from our determination, that the situation will be mastered.

Thursday, January 28, 1943
V.I. No. 26/43
I. Reich Press Chief's Order of the Day:
1. The *introduction of compulsory labor registration* for men and women will be the main feature in Friday's morning newspapers. The press has the task of giving effective prominence and emphasis to the national and crucial significance of this measure, one of many further important measures for the total mobilization of all available forces. The German people are replying to the Bolsheviks' desperate onslaught in the east with a determined action that will in future ensure the superiority of forces over their enemies. Both headline and general positioning must convey the central idea that this is an obligation toward our heroic fighters.
2. The *severe fighting on the eastern front* is to be given continued due prominence. In emphasizing the continuing heroic battle of Stalingrad, particular mention is to be made of the impressive voices of the European press.

Friday, January 29, 1943
V.I. No. 27/43
I. Reich Press Chief's Order of the Day:
1. In a spirit of utmost determination and firm confidence in victory, the German press will shape today's edition of January 30, 1943, into an impressive and rousing appeal to every German citizen.
2. The text of the anticipated *Address of the Reich Marshal* on the occasion of January 30 is to be taken from the German News Agency only; no restrictions on general descriptive reporting.

Saturday, January 30, 1943
V.I. No. 28/43 (supplement)
Addendum to the Reich Press Chief's Order of the Day:

4. Since the text of the extemporaneous *Address of the Reich Marshal* to the Army is not expected until later, newspapers are requested at present to publish appropriate general descriptions with indirect reference to the contents of the speech.

V.I. No. 28/43 (2nd supplement)
For information only:

(a) . . .

(b) The *promotion of the defender of Stalingrad*, Colonel General Paulus, to Field Marshal, and of General of the Artillery Heitz to Colonel General, is to be given due prominence, with the German News Agency announcement emphasized by career milestones and photographs.

(c) In reporting *voices from abroad regarding Stalingrad*, it is requested that the heroic aspects, the power of resistance, and comradeship be given more prominence. It would be wrong to publish such phrases as "in their death agonies the Stalingrad heroes are giving their lives in a spirit of self-denial," etc.

(d) It is necessary to advise that, *in view of the situation in Stalingrad, the sports sections of the Monday editions* are to be given as little prominence as possible. It is requested that sports items be printed with factual one-column headlines. In view of the situation, the customary appeals (to economize on coal, etc.) at the top of the front page are not desirable.

Monday, February 1, 1943
V.I. No. 29/43
I. Reich Press Chief's Order of the Day:

1. Regarding *the courageous end to the southern battle group*

in Stalingrad, the wording of the Supreme Command communiqué is to be awaited. In honoring and giving prominence to this event, attention must be drawn to the fact that the larger battle group in the north of the city is continuing to offer heroic resistance.

Tuesday, February 2, 1943
V.I. No. 30/43
I. Reich Press Chief's Order of the Day:
    1. . . . .
    2. The increasing gravity in the *situation of the fighters in Stalingrad* must continue to be given restrained prominence.

Wednesday, February 3, 1943
V.I. No. 31/43
I. Reich Press Chief's Order of the Day:
    1. The *heroic battle for Stalingrad* has come to an end. Throughout several days of mourning the German nation will honor the memory of its sons who carried out their duty to the last breath and the last cartridge, thereby breaking the main force of the Bolshevist onslaught against the eastern front. The heroic battle for Stalingrad will now become the supreme epic in Germany's history. The German press is therefore called upon to fulfill one of its greatest journalistic tasks. Taking its cue from the special Supreme Command communiqué expected today, the German press must do honor to this gripping event, outshining as it does the greatest heroic feats of arms in the history of the world, and this noble example of supreme heroism and ultimate self-sacrifice for the sake of victory must be presented to the German people as a sacred beacon. From the immortal heroism of the men of Stalingrad will blossom, stronger than ever before, the spirit and strength that guarantee the victory which the German nation is now, more fanatically than ever before, determined to achieve.

II. Further comments on the Order of the Day:
On Point 1.

The three-day period of mourning mentioned in the Order of the Day referring to the special communiqué concerning the end of the heroic battle for Stalingrad means that for this period all entertainment and amusement places will remain closed; it also means that for three days the press must reflect a spirit of heroism. The special communiqué is to be presented in heroic format and, instead of the headline being supplied by the text of the communiqué, a propaganda format is desired for which the editorial on the special communiqué can provide the basis. In preparing the make-up of the newspapers, the following is to be taken into consideration:

1. Newspapers are to appear *without any black borders* but with banner headlines. Heroic illustrations in support of this make-up may be used on the front page.

2. The rest of the newspaper must conform to the front page, i.e., during these three days a serious entertainment section only is appropriate, and there are to be no sports items, jokes, etc. Although throughout this period the atmosphere of the newspapers is to be one of heroism, it is equally desirable that *no words of mourning* appear: the sacrifice of the men of Stalingrad is to be made into a heroic epic — but without empty or sentimental phrases; the language used must be masculine, stern, and National Socialist in character. The wounds caused in many German families by the sacrifice of Stalingrad will heal. But the heroic battle of Stalingrad will outlast the ages, and it is the task of the German press to give this appropriate form. Today the newspapers wield the pen with which to write world history and transform Stalingrad into a myth that will impart strength and a sense of obligation to all future generations of our nation. From a military aspect, the newspapers are advised that the time has not yet come to describe the operative and tactical developments surrounding the situation in Stalingrad. This applies also to editorials.

Finally, newspapers are advised that an announcement concerning the three-day mourning period will appear today through the German News Agency.

Thursday, February 4, 1943
V.I. No. 32/43
I. Reich Press Chief's Order of the Day:
  1. The German press will continue to give prominence to *the heroic sacrifice of the men of Stalingrad* as imposing the highest obligation on the German nation, thus giving expression to the voice of the people. In doing so it will employ a language of confidence and give forceful expression to faith in victory.

Friday, February 5, 1943
V.I. No. 33/43
I. Reich Press Chief's Order of the Day:
  1. During the weekend the newspapers will again be guided by their strong individual sense of responsibility, and their make-up will reflect emphasis on the German nation's unshakable determination to achieve victory. The editorials, which must set the tone particularly for the Sunday editions, must sum up the heroic events of the past weeks to which the German nation is replying with fanatical determination. Germany's firm confidence in victory has been still further strengthened by the example of its Stalingrad fighters and their soldierly achievements, and under the banner of this confidence Germany is determined to grow to new strength.

Saturday, February 6, 1943
V.I. No. 34/43
I. Reich Press Chief's Order of the Day:
  1. The German press will now conclude the special *honoring*

of the heroic battle of Stalingrad with an impassioned avowal of the German people's determination to achieve victory.

Wednesday, February 10, 1943
V.I. No. 37/43
II. For information only:
   (a) The German News Agency has issued a communiqué dealing with the whereabouts of the soldiers whose units were surrounded in Stalingrad. Newspapers are requested to publish this notice in their local sections only.

Thursday, February 11, 1943
V.I. No. 38/43
I. Reich Press Chief's Order of the Day:
   1. . . . etc.
   3. An official statement in pamphlet form is being prepared in regard to the military events involved in the heroic battle for Stalingrad. Until this pamphlet is available, no more discussions on the course of the battle that might contain new information or details are to be published.
II. Further comments on the Order of the Day:
   On Point 3.
   Military sources have issued the following instructions: The heroic battle for Stalingrad is of such fundamental significance in its psychological and military effects that only a comprehensive official publication on the part of the Supreme Command can do it justice. The German nation is to receive a detailed account of the significance and course of these events in the form of a fitting document. Articles, commentaries, and editorials of all kinds dealing with the events of the heroic battle for Stalingrad, or containing previously unpublished details, are therefore prohibited until further notice.
   Sole exceptions are the communiqués issued by the Supreme Command and the Propaganda Company reports released since

February 8 by the Supreme Command office of censorship. Material on Stalingrad available to editorial offices now or in the future is to be handed over to the District Press Office. The plan for the intended document is not to be published.

(No further mention of Stalingrad in Confidential Information Bulletins.)

Manual for winter warfare

Supplement 2 to H.Dv. Ia, Page 18a, No. 17:

A. Winter Conditions

I. Influence of winter on terrain, weather, and daylight hours

1. The Russian winter brings long periods of extreme cold (40°
   to 50° Centigrade below zero), sometimes alternating with
   short periods of thaw, snowfalls, storms, fog, and poor visibility. As the season advances, the hours of daylight gradually
   diminish, often amounting to only a few hours, and then
   increase again slowly.

2. The degree to which terrain is passable depends even more in
   winter on temperature differences and precipitation. Early
   winter with strong frosts and slight snowfall permits passage
   over terrain generally regarded as impassable. Rivers and lakes
   become transportation routes for land vehicles. However,
   swamps under a blanket of snow do not freeze over completely,
   they are usually only covered by a thin crust with little
   carrying power.

3. As winter progresses, precipitation and freezing temperatures
   increase. Depending on local conditions, snow can render all
   movement of wheeled and chain vehicles impossible other
   than on beaten tracks.

4. With the coming of spring the snow begins to pack, facilitating
   all movement. However, the change between hard and soft
   snow brought about by differences in temperature can render
   conditions difficult.

5. Even light snowfall may, when influenced by wind, result in

snowdrifts causing serious traffic disruptions. These snowdrifts may start to appear in early winter and are very extensive in the wide steppe areas.

6. In clear frosty weather visibility is usually good, with sounds audible at great distances. Overcast skies hamper observation and can render the assessment of terrain and the defining of targets impossible, as rises and hollows do not show up distinctly and cause serious errors in the estimating of distances.

II. Snow conditions and characteristics

7. Snow covers the ground in European Russia in the south (Ukraine and lower reaches of the Volga) for about four months, in the central area (around Moscow) four to six months, in the north (Archangel) six to seven months. Frost lasts for a similar period. The first frosts usually appear at the beginning of October.

8. The depth of the snow varies according to the terrain. Wind sweeps away the snow from open, smooth surfaces and piles it up in front of obstacles and in hollows. In the forests it lies at a fairly constant level.

The average depth of snow in southern Russia is four to sixteen inches, in central and northern Russia twenty to forty inches. Local drifts from six to nine feet in height are not uncommon.

9. Characteristics of snow. The soldier unused to winter and above all inexperienced in winter warfare in Russia must be informed not only of the drawbacks but even more of the advantages that snow offers him and that it behooves him to exploit.

Snow, when properly used, protects against cold (see "Snow shelters").

Snow protects against wind but allows the passage of air (ventilation).

Snow in sufficient depth protects against bullets (nine feet).
Snow provides good camouflage.

10. Kinds of snow. Falling snow consists, at moderately low temperatures, of large snow stars or flakes (loose covering); at lower temperatures, of fine granules; snow is pressed together by wind (wind-pressed snow).

A crust on deep, soft snow can facilitate movement or, if it is not sufficiently strong, render it much more difficult. Stepping through a snow crust is tiring for those on foot, for skiers often dangerous. Horses and dogs are prone to foot injuries.

B. Preparations for Winter Warfare

1. Experience has shown that German soldiers know how to overcome the difficulties of the Russian winter, are superior to the primitive, native Russian even in winter, and not only can defend themselves against him but can destroy him in attack.

Essential requirements for this superiority are: mental preparation for the rigors of winter warfare; adequate training and acclimatization; familiarity with winter fighting methods; adequate equipment and/or use of improvised aids.

2. In the struggle against the hardships of the Russian winter the ultimately decisive factor is mental attitude. Many cases of freezing to death are the result of relaxing of attentiveness, of indifference and apathy. During exhaustion after great exertion, or after long, sleepless watches, the danger of freezing to death is especially great. It is then that the soldier must muster all his will power in order to remain awake, alert, and watchful. The law of comradeship demands that soldiers support and encourage each other in these efforts and in the will to survive. The danger does not become serious until faith in one's own powers is extinct.

D. Winter Fighting Methods

1. Attacks against flank and rear are especially damaging to the enemy in winter. Frontal attack, even on skis, is very difficult in deep snow. Planned preparation and disposition are even more important than in summer and require considerable time (more than twice as much as in summer). Heavy weapons, together with artillery, tanks, assault guns, have to be brought up and every effort made toward road clearing and snow removal. In making these preparations, anticipated weather conditions are to be taken into consideration (see supplement on "Weather indications").

2. Continuous attacks, aimed at depriving the enemy of rest, disrupting his supply lines, preventing him from building fires, and provoking frequent counterattacks, are proven fighting procedures in winter.

3. Since penetration of enemy lines and close combat are very difficult as well as costly in terms of lives, especially in deep snow and obscured terrain, the best method has proved to be the cutting off of enemy forces by disrupting their supply lines. The enemy is then forced to attack in deep snow and emerge from the positions that provide protection against bullets and cold, in order to free himself from encirclement.

4. Prolonged lying around unprotected in open terrain in the vicinity of the enemy after an attack that has exhausted and heated the body can, under conditions of extreme cold, lead to serious losses in human life or entail severe physical impairment.

5. – 9. . . . . etc.

Various methods of orientation:

10. The manner of orientation is subject to conditions of visibility; during the day, at night, and in fog or snowstorm.

11. Conditions for orientation are usually simplest during the day, since even very distant points in the terrain can be utilized for orientation purposes.

Points of the compass are determined according to the position of the sun. At 0600 hours the sun is in the east, 1200 hours in the south, at 1800 hours in the west (this applies to the Eastern Army). Shadows always point in the opposite direction.

12. If the sun is not visible because of an overcast sky, the weather side of solitary trees, posts, or barns which is covered with moss and lichen provides a clue for determining the points of the compass. Generally speaking, in all European countries the weather side points to the west, in Russia also in other directions (check ahead of time with compass!).

13. Further aids to determine direction are:
The direction of one's own shadow. The alteration in the sun's position is to be taken into account, snowdrifts running in the same direction (snow ridges) on broad, level surfaces (always cross snow ridges at the same angle!); ridges of hills and currents of streams that in many areas run in a uniform direction.

14. In the case of shadowless (diffused) light, it is practical to produce artificial shadows. Example: Following a hardly discernible track in the snow. A man takes up a position with a hand sled close to the track and thus casts a shadow on the track. This shadow can be clearly perceived by a second man standing behind at a distance of six feet. While marching, the second man directs the first by calling out directions in such a way that the sled constantly casts a shadow on the track to be followed.

Snow shelters:
9. An essential factor in the erection of snow shelters is the overcoming of the innate aversion to snow. The only solution is to try it out! (Cf. paragraph on "Winter conditions.")
Snow is windproof and keeps the body warm (three times as warm as wood). However, an intermediate layer between body and snow must be provided in order to prevent the snow melting and drawing off warmth from the body. (Thick under-

wear, uniform, camouflage clothing, topcoat, together with ground sheet and blanket, laid on skis, etc.)

10. Depending on situation and depth and consistency of snow, the following types of snow shelters have been proved useful: snow hole, snow cave, snow pit, snow house, Eskimo-type igloo.

11. Snow hole. This is the simplest method of quickly building oneself an emergency shelter as a protection against freezing, etc.; e.g., in a snowstorm or when an attack comes to a halt in open snowy terrain.

To dig a snow hole, a spade, skis, or even a bayonet may be used. Even when no tools are available, and if the snow is at least twenty inches deep, a man can dig a hole the length of his body and the width of his shoulders, within a few minutes, by lying down on his back, kicking with his feet, digging with his hands, and turning himself over and over. When he reaches a depth of twenty inches he digs himself in sideways under the snow, blocking up the original hole with loose snow so that only a small aperture remains. Depending on the position of the enemy and the degree of cold, the hole can be closed off entirely. The smaller the space, the warmer it is.

12. Snow cave. An even faster method is to dig oneself into the sloping side of a snowdrift. If the entrance is dug at an angle slanting upward, the cave is particularly well protected from the penetration of cold air.

Snow caves may be built for more than one man, depending on the thickness and strength of the layer of snow. The procedure is accelerated by digging from two entrances. When the cave is completed, one entrance is blocked up again.

G. Emplacement Building in Winter

II. Simple emplacements

4. When it is impossible to dig oneself into the ground owing to frozen soil, deep snow, or insufficient time, it is necessary

to build cover above ground, e.g., by stacking up sandbags. These sandbag piles can be hardened by pouring water on them. Textile sandbags absorb water better than paper ones. The walls are then covered outside with snow. The protective power of this type of cover is increased by trampling down. The whole is then camouflaged by a covering of clean, loose snow. The floor is covered with a layer of twigs or leaves. Emplacements of this type provide useful cover and are not readily detected by the enemy.

5. Round or square logs also provide a quick method of erecting cover for one or two light machine gunners. The logs are set up in an open square, their ends overlapping crosswise, and fastened together with bolts or pegs. The gunport (which must be close to the surface of the snow) is formed by leaving a gap between two logs in the front wall. This emplacement is also surrounded by a thick layer of snow or built right into the snow itself. Camouflage can be improved with white cloths (or ground sheets covered with snow); this also protects the gunner from the weather. Embrasure covering to be of white-painted wood.

6. If pits cannot be dug in the earth because of frozen ground, snow walls are to be erected. They are a protection against infantry bullets and small-caliber splinters:

Fresh snow	minimum	12 feet
Frozen snow	minimum	7.5 to 9 feet
Hard-packed snow	minimum	6 feet
Ice	minimum	3 feet

III. Barriers in winter

13. Winter also substantially affects the building and effectiveness of barriers.

Deep, loose snow provides a natural barrier. As of now, Russian tanks can cope with loose snow to a depth of three feet. Their climbing capacity is reduced by snow. Two snow walls one behind the other form an effective tank obstacle. Snow to be lightly trampled.

H. Camouflage in Winter

I. General remarks
  1. The proper use of existing camouflage possibilities and the practical application of artificial aids to camouflage can be of crucial importance for troops in winter.
  2. A continuous snow cover completely alters the landscape and conceals nuances of terrain and ground covering from the enemy observer on the ground or in the air. It also camouflages military installations.

II. Means of camouflage prepared in advance

  5. To provide resemblance to snow, extensive use of white must be made for camouflage. For this purpose white camouflage shirts and white camouflage suits (in two parts) are available; if the supply is not adequate for all fighting troops, they are to be distributed first to ski patrols, pursuit commandos on skis, sentries, etc. Camouflage is enhanced when the face is covered by a mask of white material or transparent gauze fastened to the hood. When possible, the hands should be camouflaged by the wearing of white gloves. To increase the effectiveness of the camouflage, the belt can be worn inside the white clothing.
Improvised means of camouflage
  7. Effective camouflage can also be achieved with improvised means. Instead of painting the steel helmet white, white paper can be glued to it. The ends of the paper must hang down to the shoulders and cover the face, leaving the eyes free. The paper also offers protection against sharp wind.
  8. The simplest camouflage covering for head and shoulders is made from a towel fastened in the middle (with buttons) to

the head covering, with the long ends on the shoulders. The face is covered by a handkerchief fastened to the towel in such a way that a slit remains open for the eyes.

9. Camouflage capes can be made from old underwear, sheets, torn camouflage clothing, etc., in the form of a hood with cape. It is a good idea to sew remnants of old clothing onto the inner side of the cape so that it may also be used for camouflage in multicolored terrain.

J. Protection against Cold and Snow

I. General remarks

1. In addition to the battle with the enemy, winter warfare also involves the battle with nature, i.e.: cold, snow, wind, cloudy weather, and long periods of darkness.

   The soldier must be able to overcome these difficulties not only in permanent quarters and shelters but also on the march and above all in battle. Essential to this are experience and acclimatization as well as the sustained ability to invent improvised aids.

2. The following basic knowledge (listed according to categories) is necessary:

   Clothing and equipment.
   Food supplies.
   Maintenance of health (including danger of freezing).
   Handling of weapons, equipment, and ammunition.
   Handling of motor vehicles.
   Care of horses.
   Means of providing warmth.

   The following sections deal with the above in detail:

3. The foregoing provide useful information as applied to the following (important) areas:

   Behavior on the march.
   Behavior in bivouac.
   Protection against cold, etc., in permanent quarters.

Protection against cold, etc., in battle and temporary shelters.
Firing with infantry weapons.
Firing with artillery.
Maintenance of communications.
Maintenance of motor vehicles.
Protection against chemical warfare and smoke screens.
Care and transportation of wounded.
Behavior on troop trains.

4. Generally speaking, the danger of injury from cold is slight as long as the circulation functions properly (indications: sense of well-being, blood circulating freely through head, torso, and limbs; these should all be warm and not white).

Circulation can be maintained and increased by the following means:

Addition of warmth internally through proper feeding and externally through heating; protection against loss of warmth by containing body warmth (clothing, quarters); physical movement and care of the body.

5. It is impossible to overemphasize the danger of alcohol as a protective means against cold. Alcohol enlarges the blood vessels and gives a merely illusory sense of warmth. It may not be distributed unless there is immediate prospect of remaining for some time in warm rooms. Those who have to go outdoors again (sentries) may not be given alcohol.

II. Clothing and equipment

Contents:
Instructions for fitting clothing in winter.
Improvised measures for protection against cold.
Care of clothing and equipment.

1. For the winter war in the east and north, the soldier is equipped according to plan and to the best possible extent with additional winter clothing within the limitations of available raw materials and on the basis of experience. It is nevertheless necessary for troops to do everything in their power to defeat

the cold by the proper use of winter clothing and more particularly additional methods of improvisation.

Protection against wind is equally important.

Instructions for fitting clothing in winter:

2. The correct fit of all items of clothing is essential to a proper and adequate protection against cold.

3. Principle: All items of clothing are to be fitted in such a way that a man's movements are not hampered even when he is wearing winter underwear.

Improvised measures for protection against cold:

13. Steel helmet to be provided with felt lining—preferably the top of an old felt hat, otherwise handkerchief or crumpled newspaper. Straps to be fastened loosely so as not to interfere with circulation. A simple hood of newspaper is shown in Illustration 69c, a paper face mask in Illustration 69d.

14. Feet are especially sensitive to frost. Change socks often. Inner soles of straw, cloth, or paper, lengths of straw carefully arranged and cut to fit, as well as newspaper well wrapped around the foot, are proven means of protection against frost-bite of the feet (wrinkles to be carefully smoothed out!).

19. Motorcycle riders: Chest protection against wind by flat layers of newspaper between shirt and jacket. A simple paper vest is shown in Illustration 71b. As a protection against cold, wrap the knees in several layers of newspaper crumpled to softness, worn preferably between underpants and oversock, which should reach to the knee to prevent paper from slipping down.

Methods of preventing snow penetration:

22. A button can be attached to the inside right front of the topcoat (at the same level as button provided on left front of the topcoat for inside buttoning). A piece of string is then attached to both buttons and knotted into loops approximately half to three-quarters of an inch apart. The vent at the back of the topcoat is buttoned up, the corners of the vent are

pulled through from behind between the legs and, by means of the hook supplied at each corner, hooked into the loops at a suitable length for comfort. The bottom front corners of the topcoat are then pulled through between the legs and wrapped around them. A kind of puttee made of any available material —about four inches wide and thirty inches long—is to be fastened with one end into the hooks on these corners, wrapped around the top of the boot, covering the opening, and fastened with string. The use of material from Army supplies as improvised "puttees" is prohibited.

25. Newspaper in several layers provides very good protection against cold. A sufficient supply should therefore always be carried.

To provide improvised methods of protection against cold, troops are also supplied with sufficient quantities of:

Paper hoods
Paper vests
Paper trousers
Paper foot coverings
Paper sleeping bags
Paper sheets

To be worn between underwear and outer clothing

III. Winter rations

General remarks:

2. Troops must be given hot food and hot drinks more often in winter than in summer. Every effort should be made to provide hot soup for breakfast and the evening meal. Hot water for the provision of hot drinks must be kept in constant readiness. The colder the weather, the greater must be the fat content of the food.

The consumption of food (particularly cold rations) of a temperature of less than 10° Centigrade above freezing is to be avoided. The consumption of food of a temperature below 3° Centigrade above freezing or in a frozen condition may result in serious damage to health.

5. Food and beverages, such as coffee, tea, cocoa, are generally speaking greatly affected by damp and cold.

Cold may lead to food spoilage or a lowering of nutritional value.

17. Slightly frozen potatoes are to be placed for a few hours in cold water before boiling. Solidly frozen potatoes are to be placed just as they are in boiling water and boiled until done.

33. Care must be taken that canteen goods are stored in a dry, cool place.

Beverages are to be stored in a cool but frostproof place. Bottles with frozen contents are to be stood upright until they thaw out. When red wine cannot be stored in a heated place, the casks are to be wrapped in straw mats and the bottles placed in straw coverings.

IV. Maintenance of health in winter

24. Inurement to cold can be achieved by gradual and careful increase of time spent out-of-doors in physical exertion and by moderate heating of indoor quarters, especially sleeping quarters. This hardening process must be begun before the onset of winter. There is no way of becoming inured to dampness.

Winter illnesses and first aid:

27. A distinction is made between over-all freezing and localized frostbite. The following conditions favor both over-all freezing and localized frostbite:

Lack of proper nutrition.

Loss of blood (danger when wounded).

Anemia.

Complete physical immobility (falling asleep in the open).

Exhaustion and all illnesses because they weaken the body and reduce its resistance to external injury.

Excesses of all kinds.

28. Over-all freezing is manifested in a sense of heaviness in the limbs. Walking becomes unsteady. The power of the senses

begins to diminish. The skin turns livid; pulse and breathing slow down. There is an increasing desire for sleep.

29. Localized frostbite can occur at the same time as over-all freezing, but more often alone. It occurs chiefly in parts of the body where circulation is slight, or has been impaired, or which have been particularly exposed to cold by coming into extensive contact with external temperatures. These parts consist mainly of the ears, nose, fingers, and toes; in cases of more advanced frostbite also the hands, feet, and calves. Indications of localized frostbite:
The parts affected first become pale and lose sensation, later turn bluish-red. They then begin to swell and are hard to move. The next stage is burning and stabbing pain.

V. Care and transportation of wounded in winter

Medical measures:

6. Rapid warming in heated quarters is indicated, especially in cases of generally lowered body temperature. Wounded men have a pronounced need for warmth.

7. When surgery is resorted to, the utmost care must be taken to avoid unnecessary loss of blood.

Reactions of the clergy

PASTOR N. IN BRESLAU

War sacrifices

"Take now thy son, whom thou lovest, and sacrifice him" (Genesis 22,2). In the forecourt of war stands a mighty sacrificial altar. Countless are the sacrifices made on this altar. But those who are fearful and in need of consolation find comfort in remembering others who have suffered more grievously than they, and in observing how such as they have managed to endure their suffering without succumbing to it. Holy Scripture tells us of these others. Such a one is Abraham. He is told to sacrifice his only son, whom he loves.

I. But can it really be said that in doing this Abraham endured a greater ordeal than those who today receive tragic news from the front: your husband, your fiancé, your son, your brother, has fallen? Yes, Abraham's ordeal was a greater one.

We have been *forced* to draw the sword in order to liberate our fellow countrymen from the hands of their cruel oppressors. The sons of the fatherland have been *forced* to go into battle. But where the portals of war are thrust open, there also the pathway to death is opened up. There is no choice. And in this necessity, despite all its harshness, there is consolation.

Abraham had no such consolation.

And Abraham was called upon to sacrifice Isaac *himself*, the father was required to raise his own hand against his son. How terribly hard is such a demand! Not one of us has had to submit to such a demand by God. And finally: What did Abraham know of that which comes after death, of the resurrection of the dead and eternal life? Whatever he may have dimly sensed of this, it looked like a valley in the early dawn, shrouded by white mists as by a veil.

How much better off are we! We know the One Who has deprived Death of its power. We know how in Jairus' chamber, beside the gate of Naim, in the graveyard of Bethany, He tore Death's prey from its grasp.

Do not say: But it was easier for Abraham because in the end God spared him the final sacrifice." That is beside the point. Outward surrender was far from being the most difficult part. To wrench from himself the obedient decision: Yes, at God's bidding I will truly sacrifice my son—that was the most difficult part.

2. But if his ordeal was unquestionably greater than the ordeal of those who make their sacrifices today, how did he manage to bear this burden?

He accepted this unutterably difficult task from God's hand. He was filled with the unshakable certainty: God has commanded me to make this sacrifice. So he held his peace and obeyed.

It is here that we must learn from Abraham. Whenever the agonizing news comes from the front: The one you love has fallen, the thought to which we must cling is: Now my God is calling me, now I must make my Abraham's sacrifice.

If not a hair of our head falls without God's will, how much less can a human life sink into death without the will of God! But if it is God's will, who are we to say: It is not my will? Shall our obedience founder at the very first commandment: Thou shalt love thy God above all else? Are we to let ourselves be shamed by the heathen, who have often accepted the heroes' death of their bravest men with joyous surrender because they told themselves: "It is sweet and honorable to die for the fatherland?"

A mighty fortress   Psalm 46

Be still, our psalm is calling to us, calling to us in this hour when storms are raging in the world and in our hearts! Be still, O my brothers, those of you who have to leave family and hearth and home to embark on the arduous service of nation and fatherland! Be still, O my sisters and brothers, those of you who see your husbands and fathers and brothers depart, so that your eyes and hearts weep. Be still, for the need is no greater than the succorer. Be still and fear not, for we have a God Who has redeemed us, Who has called us by our name: We are His and are certain that neither death nor life, neither angels nor principalities nor powers, neither things of the present nor things of the future, neither height nor depth, nor any other creature, neither bombs nor shells, neither barrage nor poison gas, can separate us from the love of God, which is in Christ Jesus, our Lord. "Be still and know that I am God," saith the Lord. And this God is a mighty fortress. A mighty fortress is our God—take these words forth with you, O my brothers, and hold fast to them. A mighty fortress is our God—take these words with you into your hearts, O my sisters and brothers, those of you who remain behind, that you may hold onto them and be comforted! A mighty fortress is our God. In this hour of need these words tell us three things:

In the tempest-tossed world	—undismayed and without dread!
In the cataclysm of the nations	—God is our defense and our weapon!
In war and desolation	—God is our peace!

First, in the tempest-tossed world—undismayed and without dread. Hearken once more to these strong, comforting words of God from our psalm: "God is our refuge and strength, a very present help in trouble. Therefore will not we fear, though the

53

earth be removed, and though the mountains be carried into the midst of the sea; though the waters thereof roar and be troubled, though the mountains shake with the swelling thereof. The Lord of hosts is with us; the God of Jacob is our refuge."

Verily we know not what the future will bring us of tribulations and terrors, of suffering and grief. Who among us does not think of the horrors of the years 1914 to 1918? We know not what wounds will be inflicted, what ordeals are in store for us. True, we know how strong Germany is today, quite different from 1914. True, we know we are quite differently armed, that our supplies of food are abundant, all quite different from twenty-five years ago. We know we have a strong leader—also quite different from twenty-five years ago. We know all this, and yet not one of us knows what lies ahead. We are powerful, more powerful perhaps than any other nation on earth, nevertheless we know: "Our power avails us nothing, We soon will all be lost," if—yes, if God does not come to our aid! We are protected by strong weapons, yet who can guarantee that all those who depart will return unscathed, indeed, whether those who depart will all, without exception, come back at all!? "When in the midst of life, When in the midst of war, Death claims us for its own. From whom do we seek succor, From whom do we seek mercy? Thou, O Lord, alone!" God says to us in the Thirty-third Psalm: "There is no king saved by the multitude of an host: a mighty man is not delivered by much strength. An horse is a vain thing for safety: neither shall he deliver any by his great strength. Behold, the eye of the Lord is upon them that fear him, upon them that hope in his mercy; to deliver their soul from death."

We know not what is in store for us, but we Christians know one thing: and that is our firm, joyous, strong faith that we have through our Lord Jesus Christ, we know: come what may—a mighty fortress is our God.

Therefore we say: "Jesus, walk before us, As in life we go, And we will not tarry, Faithfully to follow; Lead us by the hand, To our Father's land. In time of tribulation, Let us steadfast be,

And ne'er, though bitter be the day, Bemoan our burdens on the way. For through grief and woe, On to Thee we go. Should our hearts be moved by pain, Should we grieve for others' woe, Give us patience all to bear, Turn our thoughts toward our goal. Lead us on our way, Beloved, every day. If our paths be rough and wild, Give us succor sweet and mild. And when we have come to the end of our race, Open the doors to Thy heavenly place." Yea, a mighty fortress is our God! Therefore be still and know that I am God. Be still, O my brothers, be still, O parents and wives, fiancées and sisters, and put your trust in the One Who is your God, your mighty fortress. For—so saith the prophet —"through quietness and hope ye shall become strong."

PASTOR S. IN BRUNSWICK

Faint not   2 Corinthians 4, 7–18

In our present situation we can find help in the words of St. Paul concerning his ministry. Our epistle sounds in our ears as GOD'S CALL TO CHRISTIANS IN TIME OF TROUBLE: FAINT NOT! FOR YOURS IS A PRECIOUS TREASURE, A MIGHTY TASK, A GLORIOUS GOAL.
Side by side with the faith which embraces the precious treasure, side by side with the love which sees itself as bound to serve others, these words spur us on to faint not by turning our eyes toward the glorious goal. For those who have lived without Christ, Heaven would be but Hell! But in times when the heart grieves in darkness, the certainty of grace can light the lamp of hope and be a bulwark against despair by directing our eyes toward the glorious goal. Let us therefore heed the call from the epistle: Faint not! Yours is a precious treasure, a mighty task, a glorious goal. May the Lord God help us through His Spirit to true faith, true love, and true hope!

55

Source of strength in war

Be of good courage, and let us play the men for our people, and for the cities of our God: and the Lord do that which seemeth him good. [2 Samuel 10, 12]

Old Bibles have been found from the days of the Thirty Years' War and the times of persecution during the Counter-Reformation, some of them hidden in bricked-up holes in the wall or in hollow trees. "In some cases the lettering of the familiar sayings and promises in these Bibles is faded. The tears of those seeking solace here have caused the print to fade; the hands of those who in their agony spelled out these passages in the Bible have left their traces on the yellowed paper" (Karl Heim). What would have become of these people, our ancestors, if they had not drawn strength from their faith in the Bible to enable them to place their destiny in God's hands and to tread their path with God!

God's word, our source of strength in war

I. "Be of good courage!" This is our blessing of weapons.
  1. Yes: our blessing of weapons!
At one time the Church used to bless weapons. There has been much mockery of this. And perhaps it is a good thing the Church no longer does this. And yet we need a blessing for our weapons, a blessing for husbands and brothers out there and for us here at home; for all those whose destiny once again bears the name: war! "Be of good courage!" That is our blessing of weapons. Today we accept the blessing of this promise. With this to give us heart we embark on all the affliction of war. With this salutation the Lord's almighty hand stretches out toward us: "Be of good courage!" That is our blessing of weapons.

And yet in very truth not "our" blessing! Which of us today would dare pronounce these words in his own name without being accused of raving or empty rhetoric? Not "our" blessing but:

2. God's call!

Perhaps from afar, but do not fail to hear it! What joy: the call of someone beloved in another country, in a far-off land, but from home. Only a brief word perhaps, scarcely audible. And yet: we live on it for days, for nights—for weeks!

"Be of good courage!" That is God's call. From afar, perhaps —but from home! This is what we live on in all our suffering— through affliction and death.

3. And it is the truth!

Once and for all, under all circumstances, unconditionally: "Be of good courage!" This call of God does not stem from our own imagination. It stems from His own words; the whole Bible is God's call. The Cross of His Son is God's call to the whole suffering world: "Be of good courage!"

Toward the end of my vacation I received a letter from someone in the parish who knew I was going to climb the Grossglockner again, and he asked, half-jokingly, whether the cross was still standing on the summit of the mountain. I had just found this out for myself: Yes, it is still standing. And if lightning or the next snowstorm should cast it down from the highest peak in Germany—the Cross will continue to stand over Greater Germany, over the world—once and for all: "Be of good courage!"

A cross on a different peak had something even more to say to me this time. I climbed the Venetberg from Landeck. The most glorious day of my vacation. Not a cloud in the steel-blue sky. And on top a rare view all around of all the peaks of the Alps. But what struck me most—because it surprised me most—was the cross. I have seen many crosses on the peaks of the highest Alps, but never one like this with an inscription. And what was this inscription? "Under this sign shalt thou conquer!" *Conquer* —not suffer defeat! Thou *shalt*—not perhaps! Under this sign shalt thou conquer! Not in one section only of life's battle front. Thou shalt conquer in the world war for God and Satan, for Heaven and Hell. Conquer sin and suffering, grief and affliction, death and the Devil! "Be of good courage!" That is our blessing of weapons.

II. "Let us be strong!" That is our oath of allegiance.

1. Strong for nation and Church.

Schiller once said: "Let the Godhead enter your will, and It will descend from Its throne over the world." Faith means: to let God enter your will. Only then can our broken and fragile will become strong. We can take these words as we have learned them and apply them to the war: Let suffering enter your will, and it will descend from the throne of your heart! You must learn to say "Yes" to the war and all its suffering, to its "destiny" as being sent by God, then suffering and war will cease to sit on the throne of your heart, then God will sit on that throne, God who is the greatest of all!

"Let us be strong"—that is our oath of allegiance—strong for nation and Church! Freiherr von Stein once said: "He who will not share suffering and death with his people is not worthy of living among them!" That is the truth! But this also is truer today than ever before: He who will not share suffering and death with his Church is not worthy of living *from* it, from the values and sacrament it administers.

2. A parable from my own experience.

In my boyhood there were storms and floods on the North Sea coast. The storm bell howled through the night. The night watchman's bell rang stridently through the streets: "In fifteen minutes the dike will overflow!" Some people drew the covers up around their ears. Others packed their things so as to clear out and get themselves and their belongings to safety. But the right thing to do was: Jump out of bed! Up onto the threatened dikes! Grab a spade! Help pile up the dikes! Drag up the faggots! Haul up the sandbags! Roll up the stones! Risk your own life! Hearken to the orders of the dike master and lend a hand!

Have we today heard the storm thundering at the dikes? Will the dikes hold—the dikes of nation and Church? It is not enough to ring the storm bell! It is not enough to rely on the "night watchman"! Indeed, it is an *honor* to be night watchman on a stormy night when there are floods. That is what endows his function and his labors with true meaning and genuine honor! But it is not enough to rely on the "night watchman"! Each one of us must come out from under the covers, rub the sleep from our eyes, jump out of bed, up onto the threatened dikes, the dikes protecting nation and Church, God's dikes—the dikes of faith and prayer, of truth and love, of strength and self-discipline! Hearken to the orders of the "dike master," lend a hand and risk your life! In my North Friesland home there is an old dike law: "He who helps not strengthen the dikes must leave!" If he does not want to lend a helping hand, he does not deserve to enjoy the protection of the dike. I believe it was Stöcker who spoke of nation and Church in the battle for the threatened dike: "One drop of aid is worth more than an ocean of sympathy." This is indeed true today as between Führer and nation. These are God's words concerning His Church!

3. To the dike!

Thus speaks the "dike master." "Go ye also into my vineyard —and *labor*!" Thus speaks the Lord of the Vineyard. Yes: "Let us be strong!" is our answer.

He who can fight, let him fight!

He who can believe, let him believe!

He who can hope, let him hope!

He who can love, let him love!

He who can pray, let him pray!

He who can go to church, let him not leave his place empty in God's house! He who has a Bible, let him bring it forth! Let us be strong, strong *for* nation and Church. Strong on behalf of:

Our husbands and brothers out there,

Those who are fighting and dying,

Those who are suffering in field hospitals,

Families who are grieving,

Strong for Führer and Fatherland!

During World War I, someone sang a song for German wives and mothers:

Forge, forge, there is no choice,

Forge our hearts harder than steel,

So that they fail not in feeble need,
So that they burst not,
At times when our heroes, faithful to death,
Victory achieve at the cost of their blood.
Forge, forge, the times require iron!
Forge in steadfastness
So that out there
Heroic hearts rejoice in you!

Yes: let us be strong—strong for nation and Church—strong "in the power of His strength!" That is our oath of allegiance.

III. "And the Lord do that which seemeth him good."

That is our war prayer.

1. Yes: Prayer!

I still remember the words that were sent to us when we were prisoners of war and also in the trenches: "Do not be ashamed of the prayer your mother taught you!" He who has been ashamed, let him no longer be ashamed! He who has forgotten it, let him begin again! Prayer is *the* one great force that moves the world.

In 1871 Bismarck wrote to his wife from Paris: "When the order rang out at Taps: 'Helmets off for prayer!' a Parisian had said: *'Voilà ce qui nous manque!'*" ("That's what we lack!") Let there be no lack among us and our people today! That is your responsibility and mine.

2. "And the Lord do that which seemeth him good."

That is our war prayer.

In His fatherly hand we lay all our joys and sorrows; into His redeeming hand all questions, cares, and sins. In His hand alone are we safe with Fatherland and Führer, with nation and Church.

Gorch Fock's words spring to life again today with a sacred new meaning: "That German sailor was right who wrote to his mother: 'And if you should hear that our cruiser has been sunk with all hands lost—then don't cry. The ocean into which my body sinks is only the hollow hand of my Savior, from which nothing can ever tear me.' " The Lord do that which seemeth Him good!

3. ". . . which seemeth him good!"

That comes from His fatherly heart. Whatever seemeth Him good is hallowed by His redeeming hand. Whatever seemeth Him good is good; for it comes from God and leads to God. Whatever seemeth Him good is a blessing, even when it appears in the guise of an affliction. Whatever seemeth Him good is bright, clear daylight, even when black clouds of night cover it and hide God's stars from our vision.

"And the Lord *do* that which seemeth him good!" That is our war prayer.

CONCLUSION: THIS IS HOW IT SHOULD BE FOR US: GOD'S WORD AS OUR SOURCE OF STRENGTH IN WAR—DAY AFTER DAY AND NIGHT AFTER NIGHT:

"Be of good courage, and let us play the men for our people, and for the cities of our God: and the Lord do that which seemeth him good."

How was the
disaster tackled?

First Officer:

Q. Let's start from the beginning.

A. At the beginning of December I was still in Berlin, and it was at the end of the course I was doing there that I heard for the first time about the Stalingrad pocket from a competent authority. This authority was Major General Schmundt. The information was given out on December 6 or 8. General Schmundt began by supplying details of the pocket and the plans the Supreme Command had in mind for it. These plans seemed—and I am not saying this with hindsight, because now, twenty years later, I am smarter than I was then, but even we, who were absolutely convinced of our own powers and believed there were a number of other situations we had managed to cope with, even we were rather shocked at the fairly optimistic views they had in Berlin. So I hadn't seen the pocket for six weeks.

Q. Did this conversation take place at a staff office?

A. No, it was a report on the situation for those taking part in the course I was doing there, and Stalingrad was mentioned among other subjects. Actually the view Schmundt represented was quite interesting. He began by saying that the situation was believed suitable for an encirclement attack from both sides, from south and north, toward Stalingrad, so as somehow to surround the Russians, who were getting ready for an offensive. So all this was well within the framework of what we regarded as far from impossible. The interesting thing was that Schmundt was convinced the divisions in the pocket would be in a position to hold out for weeks with their existing supplies. Whereas those of us who had taken part in this whole thrust across the Kalmuck steppe and through the rise between the Volga and the Don knew just what state the divisions were actually in. But we felt, since after all we had considerable confidence in them, they'll realize that for themselves.

In Charkov I was held up at the airport for two days. And that was just at the time of the collapse of the Italian Army on the northern Don front.

Then I drove to R., and from R. to N. At the airport at N., on January 4, things were pretty hectic. As for the winter, though, that wasn't too bad. It was kind of medium weather, what you might call slushy. As veterans of the Russian front we didn't take it too seriously, and we assumed, well, if it stays like this things will probably work out. Then I flew in. We flew in a Heinkel 111, wedged in between bread and ammunition and all the rest of the stuff; you couldn't use machine guns because everything was packed tight, every square inch was made use of to fly in supplies.

Q. Was that a formation flight?

A. No, a single flight. Formation flights were out because there was no future in them. As soon as each machine was ready, it took off.

Q. And you didn't see any fighter planes?

A. Oh yes, we did, and then we would get down into the clouds. We couldn't see anything of the front below us because of all the haze. It didn't get really dark till we were over Stalingrad, then the clouds were gone too, and even from up there we could actually see the outline of the whole front, partly defined by infantry fire and partly by flares and artillery fire. In other words, it was already possible to get quite a clear idea of the pocket, which at that time extended over roughly thirty miles.

We landed in complete darkness. And bombs started landing on our heads right away.

Q. Was that Bassargino?

A. That was just the Bassargino airfield. In Bassargino itself things were going on quite normally. They had set up unloading detachments all around the airfield. Any special feeling, such as misgivings, or for God's sake let's hope it works out, there was nothing like that.

Q. So the descriptions of Gumrak being plastered with shot-down planes and of wounded waiting to be taken off, that would all have been later.

A. The really bad part came later. Of course there were a few planes lying around; they were moved away. The wounded were lying more or less in underground shelters or in tents. So we didn't see them either. There was no storming of planes. In other words, everything proceeded in orderly fashion. Everyone checked in as they arrived, and the pilot got the plane ready to start back again and talked to someone from the airport administration.

Q. And that was after January 4 or 5.

A. I believe it was on the 4th.

Second Officer:

A. I was sent to the division. And the division was resting not far from the Bassargino airfield. I reported to my commanding officer there. Actually, for quite a while the division had no longer been a division. Because of the pocket, half of it was outside anyway. All the supply sections were outside. Inside the pocket we had part of the tank regiment, but only part. The other group had been diverted and separated from the division. It never had been inside the pocket and was operating as an independent fighting unit. So practically speaking we were, if you like, half a division, and of this half division there was only about two-thirds still there. And of this two-thirds, the tank regiment was represented by a third. The artillery regiment was complete, although without being used as such. All the guns were lined up beside the tractors as if on parade ground, there was no gasoline and there were no shells. Of the entire complement of twelve batteries, one single battery had been got ready to move. During the next few days (January 6) the division remained in reserve, and it was ordered by the Army to set up so-called fortress battalions. This meant going to the various divisions in the pocket and ascertaining the whereabouts of any skeleton of a unit. And also finding out where any destroyed units were which this personnel was lacking, and then taking the skeletons to our divisional quarters, which, of course, were no more than holes in the ground out on the steppe, then combining them all with supply services, communications men, artillerymen no longer being used, and the remnants of battalions of other divisions and setting up a unit which was then known as a fortress battalion. And then instructing them briefly, as far as was possible under the circumstances, so that at least they knew each other and who was what, and then putting them at the disposal of the Army.

Third Officer:

Q. What happened at Marinovka?

A. We had some base-type installations in these villages where we could hold out. Then on January 10, at five in the morning, the Russians began their attack with a tremendous artillery barrage. They were trying to cut the pocket in half. It was amazing how long this went on, considering their terrific superiority. After seeing what the position in the pocket was like, we would have assumed that, with vigorous attacks, the whole thing would be over for us in five or six days.

Fourth Officer:

A.   At first it was possible to seal off the breakthroughs. Although the pressure was such that you told yourself, it can't last long. I wasn't directly with the Army, I was stationed at staff headquarters helping to get the fortress battalions ready, the 7th must have been about the last we were working on; it was immediately incorporated in the Army. So for the time being we were out of a job. Anyway, apart from that we no longer had our fighting troops. We still had a miserable little Panzer reserve, and that was immediately sent up to some breakthrough or other in the northwest, and my general and I were ordered to go south to General Pfeffer's division to serve as Panzer advisers. So off we went to this 297th Division, arriving about six in the evening. The divisional commander was an elderly fellow. I remember him later celebrating his sixtieth or seventieth birthday in the prison camp for generals. He had a wiry young lieutenant colonel. We arrived at the bunker, and the fighting involved what was known as Hill 211. When we arrived we were enthusiastically welcomed, and the general immediately said: "How many tanks have you brought along?" We reported that we hadn't brought any but that we were there to help him put his tanks to best use, whereupon he said: "Well, as for those two assault guns I have, I believe I know how to use those properly myself." So we sat for two hours in his bunker with nothing to do. We could observe how these two men with one telephone, communicating with the battalion commander, who was somewhere out there in the steppe and transmitting nothing but disaster reports, were operating with the rest of the division. What they were operating with was not battalions or regiments by a long shot, it was two groups, half a platoon, one antitank gun, one assault gun, and could you manage with a few men, and so on. But you have to hand it to that Lieutenant Colonel W., whom I still remember, he was enormously resourceful and calm. To every report that came through from outside, and each one was grimmer than the last, he at once had a solution. It was unbelievable, what happened in those two hours, you were actually present at the collapse of a division, the whole thing was taking place three miles away, or maybe five. The crowning of all this was the arrival of a reserve battalion. What happened was that a lieutenant turned up from some village or other with 150 men. The lieutenant arrived and reported with his 100 or 150 men as being ready to contribute in some way toward holding back the disaster which was getting ready to break out there. He was welcomed with enthusiasm and the general said, yes, right away, come along, I'll show you. And then he said, what's the matter with you, you're swaying? And the lieutenant said, yes, I've got a temperature of 103, and I've also got a bullet through me somewhere. I see, are your men outside? Yes, they're ready, there are some slight cases of frostbite, they're ill, too, rather. What I'd be grateful for most of all would be something for us to eat, all we've had for two days is seven ounces of bread. So before we go out into the cold night again I'd appreciate it if we could have a bite to eat. So they were given a little to eat and went off. What happened to them I never heard. Wiped out somewhere or other, I expect.

So then we drove back again.

Fifth Officer:

A. By January 13 or 14 the front had reached our quarters at D. D. consisted of two Russian houses, the rest was steppe and a few ravines. And we received orders from the Army not to retreat any farther, since there was nothing to be gained by it.

So we were under no illusions that right then and there we were to let ourselves be massacred. The first thing we did was freeze all the vehicles. That was very simple. We poured water into the radiators. And that made all the vehicles we had there useless to the Russians. With the guns, we took out the breech and poured water in there too, in fact wherever water could be poured in. Then the bunkers were cleared out. And then after twelve or fifteen hours came the surprise of the counterorder. Division assemble, march back to the other side of the railway line at . . . . The idea was to establish a defense line along this railway.

Sixth Officer:

A.   From January 15 to 22, when things had become desperate in the pocket, I spent most of my time on the phone trying to hunt up anything at all that could be used at the front. For instance, we had found a whole stack of land mines, but we didn't have the sergeant for them, a sapper who knew how to handle such things. It took three hours of telephoning to locate him somewhere in the northern barrier position. Teamwork had become very primitive. You have to remember that an army is an immensely technical affair. And all this was in one hell of a mess. All I can remember is that for about three days I was on the phone, day and night, to get something done, what it was I can't remember.

Seventh Officer:

A.   During all this time we were trying somehow or other to get personnel out of the pocket, we realized we had to try and get

important technical personnel out. We were mainly concerned
with tank crews, auto mechanics, and tool operators. We were
an old Panzer division, and it was pretty clear to us that it's not
practical to fritter away a tank crew with rifles in their hands
when they're an experienced lot and have spent the last two years
crossing Europe in tanks. Anyway, by hook or by crook we got
some men out. For instance, we got out a Lieutenant Colonel S.
who in spite of having only one arm was our commanding officer.
S. is still alive. Later he lost a leg, as well as his arm. And while
he was on the operating table in a field hospital in East Prussia
there was an air raid, and he lost his eyes because an instrument
cabinet fell on his face.

Eighth Officer:

A. Late that evening we received orders to assemble in the
central part of the city. At that time I was the divisional commander of the remnants, i.e., 250 men, and it was my job to
assemble the men in the central part of the city. I was not told
any exact point: assemble in the central section of Stalingrad and
establish contact with the Army Supreme Command. So I chose
a point on the map that caught my eye, Red Square. That's a nice
square, I said, right in the middle, too; we'll march to that point.

Q. How long did it take you?

A. It took us six or seven hours.

Q. What did you find when you got there?

A. We arrived during the night, and at about five in the morning
it began to get light. The first thing I noticed was three or four
streetcars of the former Stalingrad streetcar line, open cars standing in the middle of the street. About twenty privates were sitting

around in them, smoking cigarettes, singing, and carrying on very cheerfully. I can't remember what they were singing about.

Q. Had they been drinking?

A. No, they just had nothing to do and were waiting. They weren't part of my division, they belonged to someone else. Anyway, there they were sitting around and having a good time. We went past them and straight on to Red Square in Stalingrad. We found two cellars where we settled in, and as luck would have it pretty well our whole division, or as much as was left of it at that time, turned up there in fairly good shape. The main thing about it was that at least we were still a unit.

Q. Army headquarters were in the department store?

A. They were across the street.

Q. Can you describe them?

A. It was a big corner building, and getting there was a bit hazardous. The wide square had streets opening off it going straight down to the Volga and the Tsaritsa ravine. These streets gave the enemy a clear field of vision, so that Red Square lay exposed to gunfire. But there were a few streetcars and streetcar shelters, you always had a chance to run twenty yards and then take cover for a moment. So I got across to the building where Army headquarters were, there was a big gate; the entrance was from the rear, that's to say from the courtyard. And the courtyard side faced north. If I remember rightly, there was a sloping entrance where trucks could drive down. And then a passageway led down to the cellar. And off this passageway, quite far in, was Field Marshal Paulus's room.

Q. Did you see the room?

71

A. I saw a lieutenant at the door with a rifle, standing guard, more or less for decoration, it really wasn't necessary. I only spoke to an officer there.

Q. Were they all working together in the same room?

A. No, there were several rooms, little cellar rooms partitioned off, small ones, and some larger ones.

Q. And they slept there, too?

A. That's where they slept, they did everything there, they lived there.

Q. Did they have electric light?

A. Yes, from mobile power units. Then they gave me a platoon of air-communications people that some unit there didn't need, and we still had a few people. So that gave me a working group of about thirty or forty men.

Ninth Officer:

Q. Can you describe the headquarters building, the department store?

A. It was a ruin. The bottom edge was about three feet high, that may have been where the display windows had been. Very large, with arches on top. Facing toward the square on the right-hand side was a big gate. And you went in through this gate, that's where the sentries stood, you had to go past them. Then you got to the courtyard, turned left through the courtyard, and came to a slope where the trucks probably used to drive in down to the cellar. It was a dark cellar, you walked along it on the left.

And at the very end on the right was a doorway and that's where the staff was operating. From there you entered a large room— I can't remember the measurements—anyway, in this room, in the left-hand far corner, a canvas sheet had been hung up, and behind that was where General Paulus had taken up his abode, so to speak. You really can't call them Army headquarters in this case. He slept there as well, and sometimes he would come out, but he didn't actually take much part in what was going on in the room outside.

Q. Was it still being heated?

A. That was on January 29 or 30, that's to say during the final days. Yes, I don't think I felt cold at all.

Q. Is it true that on January 30 there was a flyby?

A. That was on January 30. That was the tenth anniversary of National Socialism, you see. And of course it would have meant a lot to the Russians if Stalingrad had fallen into their hands on that particular day. On that day, I think it was in the afternoon, but it might have been in the morning, a great armada of planes appeared overhead. It was a brilliant sunny winter's day. They appeared over Red Square, over the ruins where we had dug ourselves in, in parade formation. I can't tell you exactly how many there were, whether it was sixty, eighty, or a hundred. There may have been more planes, bombers. And there at an altitude of perhaps 1,500 feet, so that we couldn't quite reach them with rifles, and by that time we didn't have much else except rifles, not a single bomb flap opened—they just flew in peacetime formation once or twice over Red Square. It had a very depressing effect on the troops surrounded there, the fact that the Russians didn't even think it worth while engaging in any kind of combat with their planes, their air superiority. You had the feeling, if only just one bomb flap would open and at least one or two bombs would drop, so we could see that the enemy still took us seriously.

Tenth Officer:

A. The Volga front continued to remain absolutely quiet. There were no attempts to break out because there were no orders to do so.

Q. Did you know anything about the plan to cross the ice?

A. It was discussed during the final days, because things stayed so quiet in the east. But that was something only a few isolated groups were planning to do.

Q. And you couldn't say whether any men attempted it singly?

A. Oh, they did. During the last two nights men from my division attempted it, but they all came back, the whole lot, because the mines there were laid so close together that it was quite hopeless.

Q. Do you know if anyone succeeded?

A. I don't know if anybody succeeded. I only know of attempts that failed.

Q. Did they get as far as the opposite bank?

A. No, they were blown up by the mines on the first third of the ice. The mines were placed so close together.

Eleventh Officer:

A. After the Russians had closed the pocket, my division fought them off in the southern sector for a few days and was then transferred to the west and northwest near P. and D. I might mention that from about January 7 on the Russians changed their methods of attack. Until then, Russian tanks had been halted with their infantry in front of our positions, but from that day on the Russians changed their tactics and now they merely wiped out resistance emplacements with their tanks. This was how they did it: Russian tanks would emerge (January 12) from their cover and advance toward a German fortified position; thirty or forty yards before reaching it they would turn broadside and fire a few shells with their guns into this German emplacement. After that their infantry could take it easily with hand grenades. Normally the artillery fire from the tanks was enough to knock out everything in those emplacements.

I watched these tactics of the Russians through my scissors telescope for some days and was able to calculate when it would be our turn. When I reported these tactics to my regimental commander, he sent the lieutenant of our antitank unit, the division's antitank unit, over to my observation post. The lieutenant spent several days with me, and the day I knew that tomorrow would be our turn, he didn't show up in the morning. He went back each evening to his own men. As soon as it got light in the morning, the Russian tank came out from cover and advanced toward our hole. Some forty or fifty yards away it turned broadside toward us. So I said to my men, we've had it, we'll be getting a few shells now. We huddled down as well as we could in our hole, which was maybe a bare five feet deep. The first shot I heard sounded somehow funny to me. I moved back to my scissors telescope, looked out, and saw the tank burning. What had happened was that this lieutenant from the antitank unit who had spent all those days with me had been watching the scene from the slope behind, and he was lucky enough to hit this tank in the exhaust slit with his silly little old antitank gun, a 37-mm., I believe. I say lucky, because the tank had turned broadside. There were seven Russians, crew that is, and one after another they opened the turret hatch. The first thing to emerge was a machine pistol, then came a head, and so on. I used our machine gun myself. That was the end of him. Then the turret hatch would be opened again, the body thrown out, and the next thing would be a machine pistol and again the next Russian was immediately fired on.

Q. How many were you in your pit?

A. It was my artillery observation post, normally we would be four or five men in there, and on that occasion we can't have been more than four or five.

Q. Where was your artillery?

A. My artillery was a mile to a mile and a half behind me. All contact with the battery had been lost by this time since there was no means of communication. Anyway, it wouldn't have been any use if I had been in touch with my lieutenant, since he wasn't allowed to fire on my orders, it had to be on orders from the regimental commander. At that time, because of ammunition shortage, the battery was allowed to fire only five shells a day. That day the five shells had already been used up. Before the battery could fire again, it had to report to the regiment, what the battle situation was like, what was happening, how much ammunition the battery had, my battery, I mean, and then the regimental commander might authorize one, two, or three shells, depending on the situation.

Q. I see. And what happened to you then? Did you give up your observation post?

A. What happened to me was, first we took possession of the tank, that's to say we assumed the tank would still have some food in it, and we got into this T 34 tank through the bottom entrance, at least it had a round hole at the bottom where you could slip out in an emergency. We crawled into the tank through that and got hold of some Russian bread. We also got hold of some pickled herring, just a small quantity. The tragic result of the destruction of the tank was that I had to abandon the observation post because my field of fire was impeded. I abandoned the observation post and tried to dig into the ground maybe 150 yards away, but it was impossible. All we could do was dig little hollows, with a snow wall in front, and that's where we spent the next two or three days, practically out in the open.

Twelfth Officer:

A.   While we were marching more or less eastward on January 15 so as to turn south, toward K., a shot, obviously fired from a tank, fell somewhere in the group of men streaming back, men who were not fleeing but obviously just regrouping. At the cry of "Russian tanks!" these men, who had been marching back quite normally, started streaming in a wild scramble toward the east. What I'm getting at is that the infantry were being crushed under Army vehicles, the troops themselves were knocking each other down.

Thirteenth Officer:

Q.   You must have had more than that one gun?

A.   Yes, we had four.

Q.   Did they get scattered? What happened then?

A.   That night only one gun from my battery was saved, and that was Lieutenant Hummel's.

Q.   What was his name?

A.   Lieutenant Hummel. However, I was later given a complete battery again, made up of guns from other orphaned batteries.

Q. And what finally happened to your battery? Did you manage to get it to Stalingrad?

A. Strictly speaking, the battery had ceased functioning. As soon as our commander captured a gun from some place or other he would say, here are one or two guns, Battery K is operating again. And I had just got hold of the last few guns again after we had lost one gun, as I mentioned before, and two others were lost, and Lieutenant Hummel managed to save that single gun. But in the southern section near K. we were supplied with new guns. And they fell into Russian hands; it was too late to move them. From that moment on, and as far as I remember it was already January 23 or 24, by then my battery had ceased to exist. You can look at it this way: as far as personnel was concerned, it no longer existed, since I had scarcely any men left. To make up for the losses we had had, I was given two, three, or four gunners from an entirely different unit. Some of the men I didn't even know. Lieutenant Hummel, who was looking after the guns, may have known some of them. All I was told was, we've got five more men, we can start firing again.

Lieutenant Hummel reported to me, for example: "I've got two or three men for each gun now." Whereas the normal number is five, of course. Some of them got wounded somehow. So we reported again that we had no men for one of the guns. The commander then managed to allot us a few men from somewhere entirely different, and this meant one gun could be used again. That's what I mean when I say the battery had long ceased to exist as such, it merely came to life again from time to time and simply existed as a combat group.

Fourteenth Officer:

A. I was ordered to go ahead and make soldiers in a hurry out of all kinds of men: supply units, butchers, bakers, etc. It wasn't easy. It was 30 to 35 degrees below freezing, and snowing. There was no good-sized bunker available where I could have shown the men something. They could just barely handle a carbine. So then I tried to find a few men who seemed reasonably intelligent to teach them at least how to shoot with a machine gun. But anyone who tries to shoot with a machine gun at a temperature of 35 below freezing has to be a highly trained man. After four days, on January 8, I was ordered to engage in action with these well-trained combat troops. I was told a string had been strung up and that I should be able to find my way along it.

Fifteenth Officer:

A.   I stayed in the bunker, in touch by phone with my commanding officer, who kept bothering me and was forever holding party conversations, and he told me he would like an accurate map of my bunkers, so I made him a map. Then he told me, no, that couldn't be right, in his opinion and according to his information the bunker must be twenty-two yards farther to the right. The way we lit up the bunkers was by setting fire to a telephone cable. Up top we had a reel of telephone cable and just kept on pulling it down.

On January 10 a large-scale attack was being prepared in front of us to our left. Next to us lay the 113th Division, a very good division with excellent officers. The two battalion commanders, both of whom had the Knight's Cross and whom I met again later inside the pocket, told their troops: Run forward so the shells land behind you. So when it began they moved all the men forward to the front line. That way all the shells fell between the front line and the slope behind it. And on the slope behind were German tanks. Then, after about an hour and a half's barrage preparation, we were looking on like interested spectators, along came the Russian tanks. But then the German tanks were there. It really went off quite well. Then in the evening a dispatch rider turned up from the rear and told us there had been a breakthrough in the southern part of the pocket and we were to retreat.

Sixteenth Officer:

A. Then I told the men, no one is to fire, heads down, everyone, fire only when I give the order. We let the Russians come
up to within about fifty yards, we still had considerable firing
power, and then I had something like a thousand men up on
the wall with carbines and they fired away. It was highly decora-
tive the way we did it, if you want to be corny about it, and it
improved the troops' morale enormously. The Russians thought
there was nothing left there, so they came up more or less in
peacetime order, and then suddenly at my whistle they . . .

Q. A real whistle?

A. A real whistle, like on the parade ground. We were all behind
the wall, and you had a fine view over the top, and suddenly there
they all were. That gave the men a terrific boost.

Q. What happened to you after that?

A. We got out of this ravine and were sent to the Tartars' Wall.

Q. A historic wall?

A. Yes, it was. This wall, there were bunkers in it, right there
in the wall, which was like a dike, it was about twelve feet high,
as I say it was full of bunkers one beside the other, and on the
west side, what was now the enemy side, stood rows of trucks
that had got stuck there. That was where I had to report, so I
was told, so I went into a bunker where a whole lot of officers
were sitting around, all the way up to a general.

Seventeenth Officer:

A. By next morning things had become a bit more stabilized.
Stabilized is an exaggeration. A kind of assembly point had been

set up there in a few houses, after there was practically no one left of my unit, for I could no longer offer the incentive of feeding them.

Q. So the men simply attached themselves to another unit?

A. They attached themselves to another unit where they could be fed.

Eighteenth Officer:

A. On November 7 Lieutenant P. visited me at the observation post. As he was leaving he said: "You might give some thought as to how we could get through to the Volga." Two days later came the order for the attack to begin.

Q. Can you remember all this so precisely because you had come back from leave two days earlier?

A. From then on I also kept a diary. I made notes of what happened each day.

Q. The synchronizing of your attack and that of the neighboring regiment: how was that managed?

A. 576 was also able to use parts of Engineer Battalion 305.

Q. In other words, this attack took place on November 11, not 9. At the same time as yours then?

A. That's right. We started off at the same time and together.

Q. Where did Engineer Battalions 50, 305, and 162 come from?

A. Where Battalions 50 and 162 came from I don't know. But of course 305 was attached to the division. All I know is that

Battalion 305 was very much weakened. There may have still been eighty to a hundred men in it.

Q. Question Number 5 is about Statue Square, where there is supposed to have been an obelisk.

A. I didn't see the obelisk itself. But on the slopes above the Volga there is a kind of little park. There was a sort of primitive gateway at the entrance. A few scattered young trees had also been planted there.

Q. Can you draw in the position of what you think was Statue Square on the map?

A. Yes, I can.

Q. The next question is whether it was a screw-cutting machine or a lathe.

A. I haven't the technical knowledge to be able to distinguish between the two. I wouldn't maintain that it was a lathe.

Q. Question Number 7 is: Brick kiln!

A. Brick kiln was the name I had already heard. The name brick kiln stuck to it till the end. I didn't see any brick works. In my opinion it was a long, narrow building made of bricks and covered with earth. It had a semicircular vaulted roof.

Q. Not a blast furnace?

A. No, it was thirty or forty yards long. In my opinion it was more of a parts depot, judging by the shelves.

Q. It wasn't a kiln at all? That was just a term used to describe this curious building?

A.   That's right.

Q.   But it was somewhere near there that you had your command post?

A.   Later on we set up our field kitchen in the brick kiln. We had plenty of room there. It was not far from the gun factory. That's where the railroad tracks were. They went on farther.

That was the normal command post down on the flats. In action the command post was farther toward the front. We used to call it House 53.

Q.   Let's get back again to this so-called brick kiln. You gave the length. How wide and how high was it roughly?

A.   Thirty to forty yards long, four to five yards wide, a vaulted roof about six to eight feet high.

Q.   Question Number 8: What are bare furs?

A.   Those are furs where the hair is inside, the bare hide outside, so that snow couldn't get caught in it and so on. In Russia they call it bare fur.

Q.   Question Number 9: Mental derangement.

A.   There were never any scenes. They crawled away into holes, let themselves go, didn't shave, avoided people.

Captain A., for example, commander of the 50th Engineers. When he had no more men left he became, so to speak, superfluous and didn't know what to do with himself. He crawled away into the cellars.

First Soldier:

A.   All right, then, the sappers: I was a divisional engineer. With us divisional engineers, each company was assigned to a regiment to give technical assistance, particularly in connection with laying mines and clearing terrain, but chiefly we were equipped with flame throwers.

Q. You were equipped with flame throwers? You mean flame throwers were part of your regular equipment?

A. They were part of our regular equipment. In each platoon, three or four men were trained to use flame throwers, and we knew how to use this weapon right from the time of our formation. Even before, when we were with the 296th in France, and then later on with the 305th Infantry Division. Flame-thrower training was a regular part of sapper training, exactly like handling assault boats, working with compressors, laying mines.

Q. And these flame throwers were also used at Stalingrad? Where, for example? Can you tell me at what particular points?

A. I would say in the file-folder block, but I don't know. You see in November there was a lot of positional fighting.

Q. But between the houses?

A. Yes, between the houses, in the streets themselves, in fact one of the best-trained men was a corporal; he got out when he was wounded, and he was killed in Italy in 1944.

Q. Do you know anything about additional engineers being flown in during late October or early November?

A. Once, when the Luftwaffe was able to do it, we got reinforcements, and they were for the three companies operating at that time; they still existed and we got reinforcements. But I'd like to get back to the subject of the flame throwers.

Q. Yes, if you could just give an instance of how they were used.

A.   It must have been about November 11. Corporal M., from Upper Franconia, he was a specialist, was given orders to attack the sewage system, that's to say go down every manhole, the whole length of the street. The Russians were causing us a lot of trouble there, they had barricaded themselves in the cellars, and in the sewage canals, and that's where we started. I'm sorry I can't give you the exact date; it was around the middle of November. The man cleaned out the sewage canal all along the street with his flame thrower.

Q.   Can you describe how he did it?

A.   He climbed in; we gave him cover, good cover, with rifle fire, and he climbed—

Q.   Opened a manhole cover—

A.   Right. He climbed in and cleaned up the entire length of the sewage canal. They have to do that alone. What they do is carry the liquid container on their backs and hold the flame thrower itself, the equipment, in front of them. Exactly like a fireman using a hose.

Q.   So he went along the whole street—

A.   —working his way along and cleaned everything up. After that, of course, we could resume the attack.

Second Soldier:

Q.   What were you?

A.   Corporal and company clerk, in action a dispatch rider.

Q.   So you were in a position to know what was going on.

A. After the crossing of the Don in the northern barrier position we were sent toward K. to safeguard the northern flank of the thirty-mile stretch of road leading from the Don to Stalingrad North, and this took us about two weeks. After that we were sent to Stalingrad North in preparation for the attack, to the ravine near V.; that was still on the Don and the crucial assembly point. The area was called Gorodische. Gorodische was the headquarters area of the 305th Infantry Division, the Panzer Division, the Rheingold Division, the 100th Division, and the Medical Division. The general was called S. and his battle emblem was a fir tree with the letter "S." Then there was the Rheingold Division, the 113th, known as the arse-cheek division because of its tactical emblem. In Gorodische the battle alert was given on October 10. The major attack on the file-folder block in Stalingrad North began on October 14; the file-folder block was taken fairly early on, and with heavy losses. Right that first day we had considerable losses, and as the fighting continued we got to the Volga, to the White Houses. Let's see, Red October Square was before that. After the file-folder block, Red October Square, 30th of October Square, and then the White Houses, right by the Volga. That's where the communication trenches had been drawn for us, and we went along them every day, and after the file-folder block Red October Square was taken. After that it was positional fighting, all the way down to the Volga, the Volga was frozen over.

Q. It was already frozen in October?

A. No, in December.[1]

Third Soldier:

A. They were mostly younger men. I would say our company was assigned roughly twelve to fifteen men. From what I could

---

[1] It froze over on January 8; in December there were drifting ice floes.

see of what was going on, I imagine roughly thirty to forty men joined the whole battalion. They were flown in to Stalingrad without any equipment. They arrived without weapons, they were just extra men. There was even an officer, straight from the engineering school in . . . , but he was killed after two days. They arrived without equipment, without weapons. We had to equip them. It's a great pity, of course, that they had no experience in Stalingrad, and certainly within a week you could no longer speak of anyone still being there.

Q. Because the men had no combat experience?

A. No experience of any kind. For example, we worked with decoys; as soon as you raised a decoy it was shot down by Russian sharpshooters.

Q. What did these decoys look like?

A. Like the targets we had on the rifle ranges, with a bit of mud and dirt for camouflage. We knew a trick or two.

Fourth Soldier:

A. My main job was to keep a record of the dead and wounded; this was because according to regulations I had to report our fighting strength every day, our losses in dead, our losses in missing and wounded.

Q. I suppose you couldn't move at all during the daytime?

A. No, not at all. The bridge was under constant fire.

Q. Was it a temporary bridge?

A. Just an emergency bridge, built by sappers. It was under constant artillery fire from the Russians. I was very lucky and managed to get across two or three times. I wasn't wounded till I got to Stalingrad, at the White Houses along the Volga. I had to write a daily report on our fighting strength, it had to be in the hands of battalion headquarters every evening punctually around six or seven. You can imagine how they waited every day to see what fighting strength I would report. When I said: "Eight men in my unit were killed today, maybe three or four or five others missing, I have no idea what happened to them," I had to hand over my identification disks; they were then airmailed to the central registry of the German Army. This went on till about the beginning of December, and then it became impossible to maintain centralized data on casualties, the way it was supposed to work. Even so I kept running back and forth day and night.

Q. So you kept going from one strongpoint to the next?

A. That's right. I was fully informed, you see, of what was going to happen next day. We would receive precise orders during the night: Tomorrow such-and-such action is planned, it will begin at 0330 hours or 0400 hours. We will be accompanied by such-and-such units, such-and-such antiaircraft units, such-and-such other units. I knew all the details. It was all organized, and at 0330 hours or 0500 hours, when things started, I was right there.

Nineteenth Officer (Staff):

Q. You were going to be kind enough to start now with your personal experiences.

A. I'll start with the division's attack across the Don: the weather was glorious, clear summer weather, we were lying in readiness in the woods along the Don, as reserve, and were glad not to be up front for once, and we very soon found out—the attack began at three o'clock—

Q. The date, please.

A. —on August 21, 1942, and we very soon found out that the regiments up front, especially Regiment 203, had had very heavy casualties. The reason for this was that the slopes three miles east of the Don were strongly held by Russians and, using mainly infantry weapons, they destroyed many of the sections that had just come across the river, between the river and the slopes. These slopes, which on August 22, 1942, were then finally taken with great difficulty by our regiment, were needed for the approach of the 16th Panzer Division and the other Panzer divisions that were supposed to advance toward Stalingrad across the steppe. At the time we were all very much annoyed with General Korfes, who forced the crossing near V.—I'm sorry—the crossing east of V., over to our right. The crossing near V. which was supposed to be carried out by our regiment failed because of the heavy fire from these slopes three miles east of the river. So General Korfes didn't have as much trouble crossing with his division after we had taken the slopes, and he was the first to report, as far as I can remember—although I don't know whether it's historically documented—that he had taken the Don slopes. After that we formed the bridgehead, and the 14th Panzer Corps with the 16th Panzer Division advanced toward Stalingrad—but here I would like just to stick to accounts of my own regiments. There was an enormous amount of dust; there we were, lying in this bridgehead, terribly thirsty, the field kitchens hadn't brought up any food yet, and it was marvelous to see our tanks moving at pretty good speed over these slopes and across the green-gray steppe in the evening haze toward Stalingrad, everything was very dusty.

Twentieth Officer (Staff):

A. I am familiar with the situation in Stalingrad from the first day of the attack on Stalingrad; how on the first afternoon after the actual battle we moved up to the Volga; it was quite a peaceful operation, the day we made the jump from the Don to the Volga. Our soldiers were delighted to find there was southern vegetation along the Volga, with vineyards. At that point the Volga was about two miles wide, and then came the steppe, there were no enemies. We then proceeded to use our tanks beside the Volga and took the more or less unsuspecting boats under fire. It was almost like naval warfare. We were also often in that famous tractor factory, climbing around inside, from the sixth or seventh floor you could look right into the holes where the Russians were. Then during the first confusion in November we were told we had to go west to support sections of the Rumanian units that had been penetrated, so we sent off a section of the division that was still fairly strong, quite successfully, although weather conditions made it more and more difficult. On the second and third day it got worse still, since by that time we were also beginning to feel the food shortage. But actually we were still so optimistic that we said, if one or the other of the divisions comes along too, and we knew others had been sent off, we'll make it all right somehow to the west.

Twenty-first Officer (Staff):

A. The fighting strength of these reinforcements was totally inadequate, and on top of everything else we now had to share our meager rations with them. It was among them that the first signs of lack of discipline and insubordination appeared. But the situation being what it was, it seemed to me pointless to punish their insubordinate behavior according to martial law. At this point I also realized with a shock that the only possible alternative was to be taken prisoner. At my suggestion my divisional commander awarded several officers, noncoms, and men of my battalion the Iron Cross First and Second Class. I felt very honored to be able to hand these decorations to the men who had earned them.

Twenty-second Officer (Staff):

A. On February 1, 1943, about seven in the morning, I was watching the enemy from my observation post through field glasses. My adjutant called me to the phone saying the division wanted to speak to me. He took my place, and during the few minutes I was on the phone a shell exploded close by, and my adjutant was struck on the head by a large splinter, he immediately fell over without a sound. When I ran over to him, all I could do was clasp his hand as he died. Late that evening I wanted to find out by runner whether any contact with our division still existed. I sent off three runners at intervals of about thirty minutes, and when they failed to return, although we hadn't heard any shots, I realized that pretty soon my observation post would be cleared out too. I was surprised to find my field telephone still working, so I reported to my regimental and divisional commanders that I was giving up my observation post and would try to follow orders and fight my way through with my men as far as the engineer battalion bunker, which was at the northern edge of the city. This engineer battalion was also supposed to defend the generals' bunker close by, so the generals were very pleased when I turned up with the rest of my battalion as reinforcements—apart from myself, there was one officer, three noncoms, and twenty-five men.

Twenty-third Officer (Staff):

A. The night was spent in turning back the wings and making some final counterthrusts, so as to give our flanks a breathing space. The returning patrols finally reported the impossibility of the task. Everywhere they ran into assembling groups of prisoners —sections of the neighboring divisions—mixed with Russians. As soon as it got light we could see what the situation was. We were almost entirely surrounded, there were Russian patrols already far behind us advancing toward the Volga. Everywhere there were groups of German prisoners, guarded by a few Russians.

Twenty-fourth Officer (Staff):

A. Yes, perhaps there's something I can add. For the bulk of the 6th Army it really never came to a surrender. It's true that during the preceding days some divisions started negotiations with the Russians, but on the whole there was no actual surrender. One thing merged very much into another.

Twenty-fifth Officer (Staff):

A. On January 30 we tried somehow or other, wherever possible, to keep the Russians from this Red Square. And on the 31st, early in the morning, it must have been about eight, you must remember we had our own time there, the Russians had a different one, I arrived at Red Square with a lieutenant, my adjutant, and there were the Russians, with two or three T 34 tanks. And that was the end.

Q. You mean the Germans went by Central European time and the Russians had Moscow time?

A. Yes, they had Moscow time, of course. And according to the geographical latitude, all that came under Moscow time. When it was eight o'clock with us—

Q. All right, I can work that out for myself.

Twenty-sixth Officer (Staff):

A. The more it was realized that this pocket was hopeless the way it existed, a fact that, from a practical point of view, the

High Command was in a position to realize at a pretty early stage, but which, emotionally speaking, did not penetrate till much later, it was really quite interesting to see that we were all increasingly preoccupied with the thought of how, when the collapse came, we ourselves would be able to keep moving. Among us staff officers there were some more or less organized groups who speculated on how, if there should be a collapse, not before, of course, but in case of a collapse, we could carry on. There were some who said: "Where the Russians are watching least is in the east." In other words, in the middle of winter they wanted to move eastward somewhere in the direction of China.

Wounds

First Medical Officer:

Q. Before the pocket was closed, there were normal illnesses such as pneumonia, influenza, etc. What were the conditions for a soldier being sent back from the front? Was it a certain fever level (for example, anyone with a temperature of over 104 can go back)?

A. Apart from infectious diseases, particularly infectious jaundice, there were no definite orders as to when a sick or wounded man had to be sent back. Certainly the level of above-normal temperature was not the decisive factor.

Q. In connection with Question Number 1, did conditions change after the pocket was closed? Did standards become more strict?

A. There was no departure from the foregoing principle even during the time in the pocket. On the contrary, the sick or wounded man tried to remain with the troops as long as he could, depending, of course, on availability of quarters.

Q. Before the pocket was closed, were the operating instruments in the mobile theaters sterilized before each operation?

A. It was possible to sterilize our instruments right up to the end.

Q. Were blood transfusions carried out even after the closure?

A. Blood transfusions were carried out even after we were encircled, at least as long as blood supplies lasted. During the final weeks, owing to lack of blood-group tests, medical supplies, unsuitable quarters, and the cold, blood transfusions alone would no longer have had the desired result.

Q. After the encirclement, did Russian soldiers or civilians also receive treatment? Do you recall any operations? A birth, perhaps?

A. Of course Russian soldiers and civilians were treated. There were so few of the latter that treatment of that kind was simply given along with all the others.

Q. Were there any symptoms of vitamin deficiency in the pocket? Did this cause delayed blood coagulation, skin inflammation, etc.?

A. Positive symptoms of vitamin deficiency were not diagnosed even during the final period of the pocket. During the first two months there was enough food with sufficient vitamin content for these diseases not to manifest themselves. True cases of vitamin deficiency did not make their appearance until the first weeks in the prisoner-of-war camps.

Second Medical Officer:

Q. Were there any cases of mental illness in the pocket? If so, which types appeared most frequently? Mutism? Negativism?

A. Of course the mental strain to which everyone was subjected was very great. Apart from there being no hope of relief, the reasons for this were the reduced rations, absence of mail from home, the cold, and the minimum of shelter. Others fell victim to a kind of morbid optimism which they expressed by growing beards. I recall cases of hunger hallucination during the first days of marching to the prisoner-of-war camps. The men saw half-finished houses or bunkers which were really not there at all.

Third Medical Officer:

Q. In the early days of the pocket, the alcohol allocation for the combat troops was often unusually high, for instance two bottles of schnapps a day per head. Was the divisional medical officer consulted about these allocations?

A. This may actually have occurred at the beginning with some troop sections in order to clear out stocks.

Q. Was there any delousing system in the pocket, that's to say, was it possible to take any steps in this regard?

A. A delousing system was virtually impossible. Besides, at first infestation was only slight; methods were improvised such as boiling shirts or underwear in a cauldron. And sometimes attempts were made to disinfect clothing in old ovens, but this often scorched the clothing.

Q. Did you anticipate outbreaks of epidemics? Were preventive measures taken? Were inoculations still being carried out? For example, what was the tetanus situation like toward the end?

A. The last inoculation against typhus had been carried out in our Panzer division in September and October, so that there was still a certain amount of protection. Apart from that, there were cases of typhoid, epidemic jaundice, and dysentery. Antitetanus supplies were available until the very end. But that wasn't much help by then.

Chief Medical Officer of the Army:

A. I was stationed at Army headquarters near Kalach, where I was in charge of the entire medical branch of the 6th Army. That was immediately prior to the encirclement by the Russians. So that must have been about October, 1942. We already had certain problems in connection with the transportation of the sick and wounded from the positions immediately outside Stalingrad.

Then came the encirclement by the Russians. With my head-quarters staff—the chief medical officer is attached to headquar-ters, you know—I had to cross back over the Don in the direction of N., and I went to N. My own staff assembled there, and when the encirclement by the Russians was complete we had to see that the men who had been brought out as well as the ones fighting in the wider area outside the encircling Russians received proper medical care. I had no problem looking after that at N.

Scarcely had I done this when I decided to fly into the pocket. I wanted to see things from the inside.

Q. What did the 6th Army headquarters look like at that time?

A. As far as I know they were Russian bunkers that had been built for an antiaircraft division. When I got there I received orders from Paulus and was told my main job was to see that the wounded coming in were taken out with all possible safety and speed. So I stationed myself at the Bassargino airfield, then under the com-mand of Colonel R. of the Luftwaffe. There I put a medical unit to work, and they looked after the technical side. It was their job to collect the wounded from the bunkers and dugouts of the Luftwaffe and the technical personnel and to see that as soon as the planes were unloaded they were immediately reloaded with wounded, and that the wounded were looked after as far as pos-sible during the short flight (from one to two hours), and of course that their names were all recorded. In no time at all this was all running very smoothly.

Q. How were the wounded checked at the airfield?

A. Each wounded man arrived with a certificate from the dispatching depot, a transportation certificate with his name, and a description of his wound.

Q. So there was another medical officer out there who checked each case?

A. Of course.

Q. I can imagine that some cheating went on.

A. Yes.

Q. Can you cite a case?

A. It happened once that the chief staff medical officer reported the arrival of an officer with a dressing on his upper arm, so I said I would have to have a look at him first. And when I removed the dressing I found he was not wounded. He was not flown out.

Q. Was he court-martialed?

A. I imagine he was. That was not my job, I simply reported the case to Staff. These things go automatically to Staff. Since these cases began to multiply, though not much, there were perhaps five or six cases, maybe even seven or eight. The Army issued orders that officers might only be flown out on my personal signature. An officer only boarded a plane, or was loaded onto a plane, when I had personally signed the order, otherwise not.

Q. So you dealt personally with each casualty report?

A. Only officers. That goes without saying. With 29,000 wounded it was quite impossible. Obviously I couldn't deal with each one personally. Some days there were a thousand, if an unusually large number of loaded planes happened to arrive.

Q.   But surely you couldn't check every single officer and examine his wound?

A.   I didn't have to. Each officer was passed on to me with the report of the medical officer in charge, who personally guaranteed the correctness of the facts contained in the reports; and anyway you could tell—for example, I wouldn't have flown out an officer with a light flesh wound. In other words, the only casualties I signed for without question were those who were obviously so severely injured that they qualified as seriously wounded.

Q.   Did you conduct your examinations out there at the airfield itself, or were the officers sent to you at your headquarters?

A.   My quarters were at the airfield. I had to be right there. Now and again on certain days I could get away, otherwise I was at the Bassargino airfield the whole time.

Q.   In an underground bunker?

A.   No, it wasn't an underground bunker. It was what you might call a trailer, a car really, a room on wheels. It had been driven into a ditch and then packed with snow, with more snow on top, of course. It sat there with its upper part, the part with the window, above ground naturally.

Q.   That was your office?

A.   Yes, those were my quarters. I stayed there all by myself. It was so small and cramped there was only room for one person inside.

Q.   So you went across to do your treatments?

A.   No. After all, at the same airfield, some three, four, or five hundred yards away, I also had my medical unit with its kitchens and doctors. We had five or six doctors there, dressing stations, etc. I would get on the phone, for example, and call them up. You can send so-and-so many over, I would say to the divisional medical officer. He would see that the men arrived during the afternoon in good time for being put aboard the planes.

Q.   In some report or other I read there were one or two planes there but hundreds of wounded.

A.   No, it wasn't like that. Everything was well organized.

Q.   Even at the end?

A.   Not right at the end. That stopped when the Bassargino airfield had to be evacuated.

Q.   Can you give us a brief description of the evacuation?

A.   No, I can't. I said, I don't see any Russians, what's the point of running away already, there's no sense to it. Yes, they've already arrived, someone told me—January 15. The bunkers have already been shot to pieces. Again I said I didn't see anything, I didn't see any Russians. No plane's going to land here anyway, they said, it's all under fire already. It lay under fire the whole day, I knew that. It had already been like that before. At least that's what the airfield staff told me, no more planes will be coming in here, it's too dangerous.

Q.   Did you transfer then to the other airfield?

A.   Yes, to Gumrak. That's where Army headquarters was actually, but they left there, too.

Q.   How were things in Gumrak? Did you have a trailer there too, and a unit?

A.   In Gumrak it was almost a bunker, but it didn't have a very thick covering of earth; it was quite comfortable in there. There was an emergency landing strip and also an airfield. The wounded continued to be flown out. I had my medical unit there, too. It was also a big center for minor casualties, and there were always plenty of cases for the empty planes there, so they could be filled up with wounded.

Q.   But I suppose you could no longer keep as close a check there?

A.   Oh, yes, we did.

Q.   Then in the final days you moved to quite a small airfield.

A.   A very small one, just a few miles outside Stalingrad. That was the last one.

Q.   And you were there too?

A.   Of course.

Q.   How were things there?

A.   Again everything was under control. There were medical noncoms there. But there weren't enough of them to take steps to prevent planes being overloaded. Of course it wasn't good for planes to be overloaded. I didn't count the 29,000 who were flown out. For instance, that accident must have killed seventy. Probably they were included. You see, we only counted the names of those who were put on board, not those who arrived. We couldn't do that, of course, for we weren't told if such-and-such a plane was shot down en route. That was beyond our scope.

Q.   What was it like at the last airfield?

A. It wasn't an airfield, it was a strip where one plane could land at a time. The Russians were continually shooting from the edge with machine guns.

Q. What did you do then?

A. I went into Stalingrad, into the city, I mean, to my staff, to my commander in chief, Paulus, and reported to him. My task of organizing and carrying out the transportation of wounded by plane is finished, I said.

Q. Where was the staff quartered?

A. It was in the cellar of an old department store in Stalingrad, in huge cellar rooms. I stayed right there with the staff. The second or third day I asked Paulus whether he had any orders for me, I had to do something. He told me there was a dressing station in the building, I could go over there. "And if the Russians arrive, are we to surrender?" I asked. "No, we mustn't do that, we've orders not to. When that happens, go up and say, Here I am, there are wounded down below, don't forget that. Nothing more. That's all that's permitted." And that's what I did.

Q. Can you tell us something about Paulus?

A. Paulus smoked an enormous number of cigarettes, many more than was good for him.

Q. German ones?

A. Anything he could get hold of.

Q. Had he any typical characteristics?

A. He smoked all day long, really, and was usually depressed, in low spirits, so to speak.

Q. How did he behave during the time in the pocket?

A. He was always courteous and pleasant, but it was difficult to get a straight answer from him. It wasn't altogether easy.

Q. You were mentioning that you believed some soldiers starved to death in the pocket, and that you performed autopsies.

A. Reports were constantly coming in that men were dying, dying in their sleep more or less. So I ordered my adjutant to perform some post-mortems. Not full autopsies, just partial post-mortems to find out whether there had really been cases of starvation. These post-mortems showed that they had all died of starvation. The ration was, let's say, two to three ounces of bread, and for men right in the front line perhaps four or five ounces, no more. Just try and imagine that: maybe two rolls.

Q. How about getting in medical supplies?

A. They came in regularly. We were in touch with my staff, which was outside the pocket; my dispensary was there too. They had to keep on packing two tons of dressings and medicines, that's what the Junkers could take.

Q. Were these orders sent by radio?

A. Yes, or by mail, as written orders. At staff headquarters there were typewriters, of course, something would be typed out, for example, and that was put in an envelope and the envelope went back in one of the returning planes.

Q. Then you didn't have much of a problem in that way?

A. No.

Q. How about electric power? You must have needed light for operating?

A. Yes, of course.

Q. Did you have field generators everywhere?

A. Yes.

Fifth Medical Officer:

Q. I heard someone say that the wounded were sometimes placed in paper bags. Was that normal procedure?

A. No, it was not. That was almost certainly an emergency measure to try to keep out the cold. Don't forget we had no more blankets. What were we supposed to cover them up with?

Sixth Medical Officer:

A. We had settled into a ravine on the western edge of Stalingrad (roughly two miles west of the city) after receiving orders to set up a central dressing station and spend the winter there. Not far from the place we had chosen, a ravine, was a former excursion spot with buildings in more or less fair shape, the main thing that interested us being the timber. At first we were able to bury the dead properly, and we had also planned ahead for the winter and dug a large number of graves before the frost set in. But later on that became impossible, and the dead were placed in the medical unit's big operating tent.

Q. Can you perhaps recall some particularly difficult operations you performed there?

A. As I said, all the operations had to be performed at the central dressing station. The toughest jobs for the surgeons, of course, were always wounds in the abdomen, for a bullet or a splinter may cut through the intestines or the stomach not once but four, six, even eight times. On top of that, the wounded were often suffering from peritonitis by the time they reached the operating table.

I remember one case. He was a young colleague of mine who was brought into the dressing station with a bullet wound in his abdomen. He was so optimistic and so full of confidence, and then after all he died of peritonitis. I recall another case. A young Rumanian, I had to amputate both legs below the knee on account of severe frostbite, and he kept saying he was now no taller than his son. He was one of those uncomplicated, easygoing types you find among the Rumanians.

Seventh Medical Officer:

A.   About January 26 the medical unit was transferred to Stalingrad to help out at a military hospital there, and it was my job to hand over the central dressing station to the Russians. I stayed behind with some 1,500 wounded, and with me stayed my operating assistant, a deacon who is now a missionary in Africa. Then an order suddenly came transferring me and my assistant and the sergeant major to Stalingrad.

Q.   Do you know what happened to the wounded?

A.   No, not for sure. I heard later that they were all wiped out.

Q.   Did you do any operating in the Stalingrad hospital where you went to help out?

A.   No, none at all. I felt quite useless, since there was nothing for me to do. All I could do was try to cheer up the wounded.

Eighth Medical Officer:

A.   The operating bunker was connected with the patients' bunker by an underground passage about twenty feet long which a former miner had built for us, and it was protected at both ends by curtains to keep out the draft. In the operating bunker we carried out all the operations necessary under the circumstances. In addition we had an isolation bunker and a delousing station with running water; that's to say, the water was first poured into a tank and then ran down to the delousing station in the form of a shower. The whole thing could even be heated by a stove so that we had running hot and cold water. There was also a dispensary bunker.

The thought uppermost in our minds was: What's going to happen? There had been some suicides meanwhile—officers, noncoms, and men who said to themselves, I'll never be able to stand it, all that suffering ahead of us. The senior medical officer, Dr. G., had also committed suicide by taking poison. I went to the divisional staff and said: If the division should decide to defend the concrete building, I consider it advisable to remove the wounded.

Ninth Medical Officer:

A.   When we were forced by Russian shells to evacuate our winter quarters—that was January 17 and 18—we handed them over to the reconnaissance section of our division as they were moving up into position. They held out there for a few days. The commander of this reconnaissance section was a dashing young cavalry captain, he had come up from the ranks and greatly distinguished himself. One day he was brought into the central dressing station in Stalingrad. By that time the medical staff were so overworked that it was impossible to save all the wounded. The cavalry captain was severely wounded in both legs, and since there was nothing we could do for him he died, after we had made the end a bit easier for him.

Tenth Medical Officer:

A.   The following picture sticks in my mind: a tall, thin infantry-man holding a huge bone, it may have been the thigh bone of a horse, maybe of a human being, anyway he was gnawing away at this frozen bone. I shouted to him: "Hey there, what are you doing?" He didn't even hear me.

Day by day

Most attacks are carried only to the point at which the forces are just
sufficient to maintain defense and wait for peace. Beyond this lies the
turning-point, the reversal; the power of such a reversal is usually
much greater than the force of the thrust. We call this the culmination
point of the attack.

Clausewitz, *Principles of War*, VII, 5.

Stalingrad is like a painting that cannot be observed from close up but
from which one must step back in order to do it full justice. Similarly,
the battle of Langemarck was not immediately recognized for what
it was but needed the perspective of time to be acknowledged as
belonging to the annals of glory in the history of our army.

Goebbels at the Hotel Kaiserhof addressing
commanding officers of the reserve troop
sections and schools near Berlin.

Tuesday, November 10, 1942

One hundred thirty-nine days after the victory of Voronezh.
Further advance impossible.

Wednesday, November 11, 1942

Through his scissors telescope, Lieutenant Colonel S. saw Russian units, particularly artillery, in the Don forests; Captains G.,
von S., and von C. saw troop concentrations. A few pilots saw
something and reported to their superiors via the official Luftwaffe
channels. A Major M., together with some Rumanian majors, saw
considerable troop movements in the vicinity of Serafimovich.
Radio monitoring established the arrival of increasing numbers
of new Red units.

Thursday, November 12, 1942

How did Army headquarters see?

When Corporal A saw something, he told an officer. When Officer A saw something and told his superiors B, C, and D, the report virtually never went beyond the commanding general. For Army headquarters to find out about something an order was necessary. If Army headquarters issued orders to the corps, the corps to the division, the division to the regiment, the regiment to the battalion, and if A, B, C, D, and E who had received orders saw something, then the information found its way into staff maps and graphs all the way up to the Army Group. From the overtaxed troops outside Stalingrad came information that was precluded by regulations from being passed on to higher authority; the organs of the Army were designed to fend off information; it was impossible within a few days to make them more receptive.

The remaining information was distributed over six official channels: via the Army, via the German general attached to the Rumanian Army, via the Luftwaffe, via the personnel branch through the Führer's chief adjutant, via the supply section, and via the artillery section.

Friday, November 13, 1942

Who was there?

In a narrow strip winding from north to south around the Don and the terrain leading to Stalingrad: the 44th Hoch- und Deutschmeister, the 384th, 76th, 113th "with the Prussian Guards' hat," the 60th Motorized Division, the 16th Panzer Division, the 24th Panzer Division, the 3rd Motorized Division, the 94th, 389th, 305th "Bodensee" Divisions, the 79th, 99th, 100th Sharpshooter Divisions, the 295th "Proud" Division, the 71st "Lucky" Division, the 371st, 376th, 297th, the 29th Motorized Division, parts of the 14th Panzer, the "Rheingold" Division, in reserve, the 9th Antiaircraft Division, as well as Rumanian and Croatian units.

Saturday, November 14, 1942

Forty-seven days after the minor victory of Orlovka.

Did Paulus know the Army was immobilized?

He observed that it did not advance. That did not necessarily mean it was immobilized. Perhaps it would soon start advancing again.

Sunday, November 15, 1942

Commanding General "Optimist" S. laughed when he heard rumors among the officers that the Russians were in the Don forests. Press directive of Chief of General Staff Zeitzler in Wolfs-schanze: "The Russians are now crucially weakened."

Monday, November 16, 1942

Organization for Stalingrad:

Hitler

Zeitzler

von Bock ➤ von Weichs ➤ von Manstein

Paulus

Chief of Staff: Schmidt

Von Seydlitz   Heitz   Strecker   Jaenecke   Hube

Edler von Daniels, Pfeffer, Stempel, Alexander von Hartmann, S., L., R., Dr. Renoldi, Schlömer, Wulz, B., etc., down to Corporal Wille, Privates First Class Tacke, F., B., etc.

Tuesday, November 17, 1942

Climate among the leaders:

Colonel General von Richthofen telephoned Jeschonnek, Jeschonnek telephoned Göring, Göring telephoned Schmundt, and Schmundt telephoned the Führer: the commanding officers at Stalingrad were weak. General von Seydlitz considered Paulus's attitude and most of his decisions mistaken. Divisional Commanders L. and von K. could not stand each other; conflicts in the issuing of orders existed between a divisional commander and his commanding general. The generals were united in one thing: eyes shut, and utmost efforts exerted in the attainment of victory.

Wednesday, November 18, 1942

Were Paulus and his staff aware of any danger?

When he wanted a breath of air, Paulus often used to stand in front of his headquarters in Golubinskaya. From there to the northeast he could see a little wood. Muddy paths led to his command post. When he looked through his binoculars he could just make out the valley of the Don. On maps showing the position of the enemy, Paulus saw more and more Red entries; it was said the Russians had simply split their units in half.

The ground at the military airfields is soft; personnel gets mixed up at the overloaded airfields, the chain of command becomes confused.

Low clouds, driving snow, very poor visibility. The Rumanians are complaining.

Thursday, November 19, 1942

The Russians attacked very early on 19th, keeping well beyond the edges of the Army. Two breakthroughs beyond the Army's sphere of authority.

At 6 P.M. Paulus reported to his superiors his intentions for November 20: continued assault troop activity in Stalingrad.

5th Panzer Artillery Regiment 16 fired on gunboats on the Volga; fortifications on the other side of the Volga were also taken under fire.

In Stalingrad, unfavorable flying weather.

Near Maikop in the Caucasus, good flying weather, Colonel General von Richthofen therefore active there with his pilots. Hitler in South Germany. Göring in Paris. Zeitzler in East Prussia.

Field Marshal von Manstein in Vitebsk. The staff of the 6th Army with Paulus in Golubinskaya. Colonel General von Weichs with Sodenstern in Starobelsk, he immediately sized up the danger of the situation correctly.

Friday, November 20, 1942

South of Stalingrad, near Lake Tsatsa, the Russians sent in their second group; here again the Rumanians involved had no idea why they were supposed to let themselves be wiped out. A few hours later, Colonel General Hoth, who was in command, was without an army and had to evacuate his headquarters hurriedly. The leaders of the 4th Rumanian Army were not ready to take over the supreme command in Hoth's place that day. Into this confused situation drove the combat-experienced 29th Motorized Division. It was foggy. The order read: "The 29th Motorized Infantry Division will prepare during the night of November 19/20 for an attack toward the south, and on the morning of November 20 will throw back and destroy the enemy, who has penetrated in the south, by attacking in the direction of Elista." When the fog lifted the following sight was presented: Along a railroad track, toward the south, long freight trains filled with Russian infantry. Flocks of tanks, tanks driving around everywhere. The well-rested 29th Division engaged in action as if in open battle until 5 P.M.

The 6th Army command was first preoccupied with the comparatively nearby breakthrough of the previous day near Kletskaya (north). Paulus silently studied his maps. "Bloody disgrace," said Schmidt. Bloody disgrace, said General of the Infantry Strecker. Bloody disgraceful business that was, said General of the Artillery Heitz to his officers. Looks to me like a bloody disgrace on the Don, said Major General Leyser when he heard the cannons booming. A pretty bloody disgrace, said Pfeffer. General Hube said on the telephone: I say it's a bloody disgrace! I won't accept that, it must be ironed out, said Zeitzler on the telephone before he grasped the whole extent of the danger. A bloody disgrace, said von Seydlitz, K., Wulz, etc.

What happened?

With their stronger, western, Serafimovich breakthrough group, which now began to appear more distinctly on the German maps, the Russians gained a further thirty-five miles. The 48th Panzer Corps, practically a whole Panzer regiment, had been placed in position as a reserve against the Russians. It was equipped with captured tanks. Mice were said to have eaten into the interior equipment of the tanks. As the trucks drove through D. and T., the order came at twelve noon to attack toward the northwest.

What did the unfortunate corps do?

It turned off to the left from the road along which it was marching. All the units got mixed up. Radio contact was disrupted. In this state the corps ran ahead on into the 5th Russian Tank Army, which was advancing via Blinoff. The order came to retreat to the River K. En route the corps received orders to halt. Then came an order to attack to the north, then an order to form hedgehog positions, then an order to attack to the northeast, then an order to wait. The corps was desperate, the corps commander was arrested soon after and was to be shot.

1/79, 1/64, parts of 5 and 10/64, 11/64, K16, parts of Artillery Regiment 16, remains of the 2nd Panzer Regiment, and the then mobile sections of the 6th Army, assembled at dawn near Orlovka. The snow was knee deep. After thirty-five miles quick march through the "corridor" between the Volga and the Don, dark dots appeared in the west, large groups of men moving eastward, some of them without weapons. An hour later the roads were choked. During the night of the 20th/21st, the above-named sections of the Army crossed the Don bridge near Gorodische. Advance patrols hurried to Suwalki. The tank treads were not equipped with antiskid lugs. The heavy vehicles, more like iron boxes here, skidded right across the mirror-smooth road leading along the Don heights. Numerous orders: Set up a defense front along the stream sector southwest of Gorodische! A few minutes later: About-face, march! Soon after that: As you were; advance!

During the night the Russians turned their northern, northwestern, and southern pincers by ninety degrees each. They were now marching on Kalach. In the 6th Army, lively telephone communication on all command levels until well into the night. General Paulus got practically no sleep; his chief of staff, General Schmidt, slept about two hours. The Russian tanks drove throughout the night in order to make full use of the engines.

As an immediate step Hitler appointed Field Marshal von Manstein commander in chief of a newly formed Don Army Group. Due to weather conditions, von Manstein chose to travel by train rather than plane.

Before long the Army Group in process of formation disposed over the following troops:

One Italian expeditionary corps.

Fleeing Rumanians of the 3rd Army.

Combat Group Philipp.

Combat Group Tschökelt.

Combat Group von Burgsdorff.

Two 100-mm. guns.

Supreme command over an encircled army.

Group Hollidt, later also: Fretter Pico.

One armored train moving north from Rostov.

4th Panzer Army.

The 4th Panzer Army disposed over:

1,200 Rumanian cavalrymen.

A few antiaircraft guns.

Six damaged tanks.

Saturday, November 21, 1942

When General Constantinescu, till then deprived of the supreme command of the 4th Rumanian Army by the temperamental German Colonel General Hoth, assumed command in the south at noon on November 21, his army had been reduced by half. Hoth's final action had been to send the last fresh unit into battle, i.e., two-thirds of the 8th Rumanian Cavalry Division stationed behind the hills of K.

Bad weather continued during the afternoon. Air Force General von Richthofen came to the conclusion that "a period of good weather combined with intensive action on our part will smash this Russian affair."

Much movement among the entire Army staff. Telephoning throughout the day. I don't see any threat to the bridge at Kalach, said General Schmidt, since the slopes of Kalach are adequately manned to safeguard the bridge.

Two generals appear and announce misgivings. Schmidt sends them about their business: "Rubbish, gentlemen. . . ."

In the afternoon, telephone conversations with Sodenstern, who has had misgivings about the situation from the very beginning. Near Kalach, already threatened by the enemy, Lieutenant General G. came upon a bakery column that had no idea what was going on. Excellent fresh bread! The lieutenant general did not want to alarm the column and spoke reassuringly.

In the morning about forty Russian tanks appeared in front of the bridgehead at Kalach. When they were driven off there, they appeared at noon on the high west bank of the Don, near Army headquarters at Golubinskaya. Now the Army commanders saw the danger.

Sunday, November 22, 1942

Army staff at Golubinskaya is on the telephone until 11 A.M. At twelve noon the headquarters transport squadron flies ahead into the pocket that is forming; Commander in Chief Paulus and his chief of staff fly to Nizhniy-Chirskaya. There, at 1 P.M., Colonel General Hoth, commander of the beaten 4th Panzer Army, drives up. At the Army command post at Nizhniy-Chirskaya, intended as Paulus's winter quarters, commanding officers Hoth and Paulus consult with their staff officers.

At 2 P.M. General Paulus leaves the fully-equipped command post of Nizhniy-Chirskaya and flies with his chief of staff into the pocket that is forming. The Army command post is set up in small earth bunkers near the Gumrak railway station. While the commander and his chief of staff quickly wash their hands, their staff officers set up a map table. Paulus told Schmidt, as he looked at the maps: "We'll separate now for an hour; we'll each give the matter some thought. Then we'll meet again here and exchange views."

They considered what they would do. They decided in the end to break out toward the southwest.

Paulus's command post: a mile and a half west of Gumrak railway station, four to five miles from Stalingrad: twelve pits dug into the ground, six feet deep, irregularly distributed in a circle of fifty to eighty yards. General Paulus's pit was twelve feet by twelve. It was covered by a layer of earth six feet deep and frozen hard, with sturdy supporting beams. Equipped inside with planks and improvised material. Clay oven. Draft screens at the entrances. Later on the approaches to the headquarters became recognizable from the air; until then the headquarters was considered well camouflaged. But since Russian enemy reconnaissance was not particularly good, Generals Rokossovski and Voronov did not know until close to the end where their enemy Paulus actually was.

On the afternoon of November 22 General von Seydlitz, in command of the LI Army Corps, turned up at Paulus's command post and proposed an immediate breakout. Paulus referred him to the requests already submitted to the Supreme Command and the further measures intended.

At 6 P.M. General Paulus sent the following radio message to Army Group B:

Army surrounded. Entire Tsaritsa[1] valley, railway from Sovietskiy[2] to Kalach, Don bridge there, slopes along the west bank of the Don as far as Golubinskaya, Olskinskiy,[3] and Krainiy in Russian hands despite heroic resistance. Additional forces proceeding from the south-

[1] What is apparently meant is not the Tsaritsa in Stalingrad but the Donskaya Tsaritsa.
[2] Same as railway station at Krivomuskinskaya.
[3] Two and a half miles southwest of Osinkiy.

east via Buzinovka northward and especially strong from the west. Situation near Surovikino and Chir unknown. Stalingrad and north front strong reconnaissance activity, attacks on IV Army Corps fought off and on 76th Division. Minor breakthroughs there. Army hopes to be able to build up western front east of the Don in the Golubaya sector.[4] Southern front east of the Don still open. Doubtful whether it can be closed by intensive weakening of the northern front to build up thin line from Karpovka via Maimovka, Golubinskaya. Don frozen and passable. Fuel almost exhausted. Tanks and heavy weapons will then be immobilized. Ammunition position strained. Rations for six days. Army intends holding remaining area from Stalingrad to Don and has taken all necessary measures. Essential to this is successful closing of southern front and ample provisions being flown in. Freedom of action in case hedgehog formation unsuccessful. Situation may then compel abandoning Stalingrad and northern front so as to strike enemy on southern front with all possible force between Don and Volga and establish contact there with 4th Panzer Army. Attack westward not promising due to enemy strength and difficult terrain.

Lieutenant H. reports:

Nonbelief in nonvictory.

November 22, Remembrance Sunday, foggy. Our vehicles stood in a long column on the road through the village of T. At 8 A.M. we heard tanks advancing out of the fog toward the village. We fled to a water ditch. The tanks went around the village and drove into the Rumanians fleeing, screaming, on the main highway to Marinovka; this gave us a moment's respite. The vehicles that could be started up first drove clear across the fields to Marinovka. We halted in a hollow. The soldiers climbed the edge of the hollow and looked back. Of those who had been at T. the following were present: Captain J., Staff Medical Officer B., First Lieutenant Krull, Senior Paymaster Meier, Ensign (Eng.) Mehns, Ensign Köstler, Sergeant Keller, Sergeant Bernhard, Sergeant Lorenz, Staff Corporal Wilmes, Corporals Wittl, Mai, Hohmann, Verheyen, Hinz, Kradepohl, Mohrenweiser, Privates First Class Pfeifer, Teichert, Schwiers, and Rühmenapp.

[4] Unclear; east of the Don there is no Golubaya sector.

Major L. reports:

Quarters in Marinovka were overcrowded. Flight movements in the direction of Kalach (west) and Stalingrad (east). We certainly did not regard this confusion as a final disaster. We saw Russian tanks blocking the supply route east of Marinovka. In Karpovka we found conditions similar to those in Marinovka. With the aid of the military police, the local commander in Karpovka tried to man a line of defense. At dawn Privates First Class M. and W. were ordered by Captain J. to burn all secret documents and service regulations. Another group brought in two demijohns of schnapps and a truckload of white bread. An order issued by a section of the divisional staff reached us. Near Orlovka we occupied a hollow. To our right lay the paratrooper combat group Matuk.

Captain W. reports:

Corporal L. of the 2nd Panzer Artillery Regiment 16 went to get some wood (the division was drawn up on the road leading along the Don heights). A hundred yards away from the firing position L. fell into the hands of a Russian reconnaissance patrol. He was shot by a pistol through the jaw and had the presence of mind to sham dead.

First Lieutenant R.:

Burning vehicles everywhere. Vehicles broke through the ice trying to cross the partly frozen Don. Lame horses could be exchanged for saddled riderless horses.

Lieutenant General F. was traveling across the pocket area and, as far as it was possible to gain an impression from his vehicle, seemed to see moving or firing tanks coming from all directions.

The spearheads of the 51st Russian Assault Army (south) and the 5th Tank Army (strong western North Group) joined forces during the latter part of the morning. Late that evening Hitler left Obersalzberg by special train for Leipzig; before leaving he gave orders that the 6th Army was to take up positions on the bank of the Volga.

Monday, November 23, 1942

Weather along the Donets somewhat improved. In the breakthrough area, bad weather.

Field Marshal von Manstein en route with his officers in an official train heading for the breakthrough area.

Chief of General Staff Zeitzler sent Lieutenant Colonel (General Staff) Coelestin von Zitzewitz to the Stalingrad area to report back to him: "I want you to send me as many reports as you can, directly and speedily. You have no executive functions of any kind. We are not worried; General Paulus is managing very nicely."

Paulus's radio message in the evening:

Secret orders—top level

Radio message to Supreme Command
By way of Information: to Army Group B.

My Führer,

Since receipt of your radio message on the evening of November 22, events have succeeded each other precipitately. The closing off of the pocket in the west and southwest failed. There are indications of imminent enemy breakthroughs.

Ammunition and fuel are nearly exhausted. Numerous batteries and antitank weapons are out of ammunition. There is no prospect whatever of adequate supplies arriving in time.

The Army very soon faces annihilation unless all forces are combined to deal a mortal blow to the enemy attacking from the south and west.

For this purpose it is necessary immediately to withdraw all divisions now in Stalingrad as well as strong forces from the northern front. The inevitable result must be a breakthrough to the southwest, as the eastern and northern fronts cannot be held if weakened to such an extent.

Although this will mean the loss of a great deal of equipment, we shall conserve the majority of valuable fighting men and at least part of the equipment.

In stating that Commanding Generals Heitz, Strecker, Hube, Jaenecke, and von Seydlitz have arrived at the same assessment of the position, I retain full responsibility for this vitally important report.

On account of the situation, again request freedom of action.

> Heil my Führer!
> (signed): Paulus.
> November 23, 2130 hours.
> Transmitted to the Supreme Command:
> November 23, 2345 hours.
> For the accuracy of this copy:
> Lieutenant

That evening General von Seydlitz ordered a certain sector in the north of Stalingrad to be evacuated without informing Army headquarters; all equipment not required for the impending breakout to the southwest was burned or destroyed on his orders.

Zeitzler telephoned von Sodenstern at 2 A.M., saying he believed he had now convinced Hitler.

Colonel General von Weichs was asleep, Paulus was trying to sleep, Schmidt was asleep, von Sodenstern waited until 4 A.M. for a further call from Zeitzler.

After that, Schmidt, Paulus, von Weichs, von Sodenstern (also for part of the time Zeitzler in Wolfsschanze) waited for the order to break out. The breakout could then have been completed by about the 28th.

Toward noon of the following day Zeitzler telephoned; Sodenstern thought he detected from his voice that there had been a difference of opinion with Hitler.

Tuesday, November 24, 1942

The outline of the pocket is as follows: southern end of Kuperosnoye—Volga bank as far as five miles northeast of Kuperosnoye —turning away from the Volga opposite the steamer ferry to Krasnaya Sloboda and running at a distance of about three-quarters of a mile from the bank in a northeasterly direction—after six miles again touching the Volga—three miles along the bank to Rynok—southwestern edge of the Rynok balka (ravine) to Point 139—peak three and a half miles southeast of Kotluban railway station—Point 133—two miles north of Point 137—crossroads six miles southwest of Kotluban village—Point 124 (three miles northwest of Baburkin)—Point 127 (two miles north-northeast of Dmitriyevka)—Point 135 (three miles west-southwest of Dmitriyevka)—Point 118 (three miles of Illarionovskiy)—western and southern edge of Marinovka—southern edge of Prudboi—along the projected railway west of Rokotino—west of Tstsbenko—three-quarters of a mile south of Tsybenko—north of and close to Yagodniy—Yelchi—south of Novaya Peschanka—Kuperosnoye.

The city of Stalingrad stretches for several miles along the west bank, the so-called hilly bank, of the Volga, i.e., the eastern edge of the Volga–Don plateau. The area is flat and treeless. Every twenty to twenty-five miles the terrain is broken by a stream in a steep-sided valley. These valleys contain the villages with groups of trees. There are also eroded ravines known as balkas. The distance between villages or cottages is seldom more than twenty miles. In winter, prolonged northeasterly storms prevail. Several planes were torn away by the gale on an airfield south of Stalingrad. The snow is not particularly deep, but drifts can accumulate up to 300 feet in width. The temperature seldom drops below 40 degrees of frost; however, spectacular drops in temperature frequently occur, often of more than twenty degrees within a few hours. Both the Don, with its heavily wooded valley six miles wide, and the broad Volga form weather divides, so that west of the Don it is impossible to tell what the weather is like in Stalingrad. Conditions for survival and shelter on a large scale exist only in the city of Stalingrad and in the Marinovka valley, the extreme western loop of the pocket. The terrain slopes gently from west to east. Any existing hills are to be found only in some dip in the terrain; hence they are not visible from a distance.

Weather on the 24th somewhat more favorable. Fighter plane units were dispatched to harass Russian columns.

Soon after 10 A.M. the outgoing telephone lines were cut.

General von Seydlitz sent Paulus a memorandum. A note was added to this memorandum by Army Chief of Staff General Schmidt: "General von Seydlitz should not try to take on the worries of the Commander in Chief, and the latter not those of the Führer." The file was passed on through official channels to von Weichs and Sodenstern, who did not pass it on to Hitler. Von Manstein arrived in Starobelsk at von Weichs' headquarters; talks with von Weichs and Sodenstern. From von Weichs' room von Manstein dispatched a radio message to Paulus: "Doing everything to get you out." He gave orders to remain on the bank of the Volga. In a telephone conversation with Zeitzler, von Manstein said: "I wish it to be clearly understood that, unless there is a certainty of supplies arriving, we must not risk leaving the 6th Army where it is, for it is probably still possible for the Army to break out toward the southwest." Once again von Manstein boarded his official train for Charkov. At Wolfsschanze, discussions between Hitler, Zeitzler, Field Marshal Keitel, Colonel General Jodl, Reich Marshal Göring, Jeschonnek.

Colonel General Jeschonnek, Chief of General Staff of the Supreme Commander of the Luftwaffe, demanded immediate support from the central meteorological branch in rebutting accusations made in the Supreme Command of the Armed Forces against the meteorological branch in connection with inaccurate data on the Russian winter. It was established that in September a memorandum composed by Dr. D. had been transmitted by the General Staff of the Luftwaffe to the Supreme Command. It had been emphasized in this memorandum that even the mildest Russian winter was much more severe than the severest Central European winter. Hence in Jeschonnek's opinion the Supreme Command must have received reports from other sources. It is assumed that these may have been reports on Russia drawn up by military geographers which had been submitted to the staff of the Supreme Command with the omission of important warning phrases.

Göring and Jeschonnek considered that supplying of Stalingrad from the air was on the whole feasible. Zeitzler doubted it.

The Russians believed they had surrounded 80,000 men; Supreme Command staff: roughly 400,000. The quartermaster of the Army said later: 300,000. Paulus believed he had about 200,000 men under him.

Wednesday, November 25, 1942

Overnight the ground froze solid.

General Paulus intended to follow the orders issuing from outside the pocket. Had he acted otherwise he would have had a very poor opinion of himself. "To act contrary to the plans of the command as a whole can, if it becomes a system, lead to anarchy in the command."

"What's the good of talking?" said General Schmidt. "I don't see any easy solution."

Göring represented a last hope. Perhaps he would have an inspiration?

General von Seydlitz:

At the end of November, von Seydlitz could have been Commander in Chief of the Army. Since he did not occupy this post, he found himself in a false position. Now, before dawn on the 25th, a radio order of Hitler's came through appointing General von Seydlitz commander of the northern front (over Paulus's head). Field Marshal General von Manstein, en route to his forward headquarters, immediately protested the order. Von Manstein's protest received no formal reply. In practical terms, however, the protest was to be interpreted, effective the 28th, as a counterorder depriving von Seydlitz of what Hitler had bestowed on him. Generals Paulus and von Seydlitz met personally that day.

Thursday, November 26, 1942

Minor casualties back to their units. A soldier whose eyes had been destroyed would not let go of the doctor's hand. Funeral procession with the most seriously wounded on the road from Marinovka to Karpovka.

Paulus wrote a letter to von Manstein:

Commander in Chief of the	Gumrak Railway Station
6th Army	November 26, 1942
For submission to the	
Commander in Chief and	
Chief of Staff	Written by an officer

Field Marshal von Manstein
Commander in Chief of the Don Army Group

Dear Field Marshal,
I. Thank you for your radio message of November 24 and the assurance of assistance.
II. To help you in assessing the situation I wish to report the following:
    1. When the major Russian offensives against the Army's right and left neighbors began on November 19, the Army's two flanks were exposed for two days, and here the Russians rapidly advanced with their mobile forces. The spearheads of our own mobile units (14th Panzer Corps) moving westward across the Don encountered a superior enemy west of the Don and found themselves in a very difficult position, especially as their mobility was severely hampered due to fuel shortage. Simultaneously the enemy advanced into the rear of the XI Army Corps which, acting on orders, had held its position toward the north to the fullest extent. Since it was no longer possible to withdraw any forces from the front to ward off this threat, the only possible course was to swing the left wing of the XI Army Corps toward the south and allow the Army Corps temporarily to retreat and take up a bridgehead position west of the Don, in order to prevent those of its units occupying positions west of the Don from being split off from the bulk of the Army.

      While these measures were being carried out, an order from the Führer arrived demanding an attack on Dobrinskaya by the left wing of the 14th Panzer Corps. This order had been rendered obsolete by events. I was therefore unable to carry it out.

2. On the 22nd, the IV Army Corps, until then under Panzer Army High Command 4, was also placed under my command. The right wing of the IV Army Corps was retreating from south to north via Buzinovka. This left the whole southern and southwestern flank exposed. If the Russians were not to advance unopposed into the rear of the Army in the direction of Stalingrad, the only course was to withdraw forces from Stalingrad and the northern front. There was a good chance of these being brought up in time, while it could not be done with forces from the area west of the Don.

With the aid of the forces moved up by us from the Stalingrad front to join the IV Army Corps, the latter succeeded in building up a weak southern front with its west wing near Marinovka; however, on the 23rd this front was penetrated by the enemy at a number of points. Outcome still uncertain. On the afternoon of the 23rd, strong enemy armored units, including 100 tanks, were observed in the area west of Marinovka and repeatedly confirmed. In the whole region between Marinovka and the Don there were only scattered German strongpoints. The way lay open for Russian tanks and motorized forces, likewise in the Pestkovatka area toward the Don bridge.

For thirty-six hours I had received neither orders nor information from my superiors. Within a few hours I might have found myself in the following position:

(a) Either holding my position with the western and northern fronts and watching the Army front very soon being rolled up from behind, in which case I would be formally obeying the order given me to hold my positions, or

(b) take the only decision possible in such a situation and turn with all available forces against the enemy that was about to stab the Army from behind. Needless to say, in that case the eastern and northern front could no longer be held and the only possible course would then be a breakthrough toward the southwest.

In the case of (b), although acting in conformity with the situation, I would be guilty—for the second time—of disobeying an order.

3. In this critical situation I dispatched a radio message to the Führer requesting freedom of action for an ultimate decision

of this kind when necessary. In requesting such authorization I was looking for backing so that I would not come too late with the only feasible order under the circumstances.

That I would only give such an order in case of extreme necessity and not prematurely is something for which I can offer no proof: I can only ask for confidence.

I have received no direct reply to this radio message. . . .
III. Today's position is being transmitted on a map. Although it was possible to move additional forces up to the southwestern front, the situation there remains critical. . . . The Stalingrad front is daily resisting strong enemy pressure. . . .

The air supplies of the last three days have provided only a fraction of the calculated minimum requirements (660 tons = 300 Junkers a day).

Within the next few days, shortage of supplies may lead to a crisis of the utmost gravity.

Nevertheless I believe the Army can hold out for some time. But whether the daily increasing weakness of the Army, combined with lack of shelter as well as of lumber and firewood, will make it possible to continue to hold the area around Stalingrad —even if a corridor were to be opened up to me—is something that it is impossible to judge at present.

Since I am besieged every day with many very natural inquiries about the future, I would appreciate receiving more data than hitherto in order that I may bolster the confidence of my men.

May I say, Field Marshal, that in your command I find assurance that everything possible is being done to assist the 6th Army. . . .

Yours obediently,
(signed): Paulus

Please excuse the informality of paper and handwriting, both attributable to present circumstances.

Friday, November 27, 1942

For some weeks the transport trains of the 6th Panzer Division had been arriving in Russia from western France. At 8 A.M. the first transport train appeared at the Kotelnikovo railway station, which was already under artillery fire.

For a few hours that morning, tanks of the 6th Army continued along the west bank of the Don. Then they left this bank. Seven hundred vehicles were abandoned to the Russians.

"Clinging to the ground with his nails"
G. clung with his nails to the frozen ground, a nail broke. The tank watched, then rolled over G.

That day Hitler stated that "the prospects in Stalingrad were excellent." After others had made mistakes, von Manstein, full of self-confidence, assumed command of the Don Army Group on the 27th, effective the morning of the 28th.

The Supreme Command replied that day by teletype to the report of former Army Group B on its appraisal of the situation as of November 24.

Saturday, November 28, 1942
Field Marshal von Manstein immediately submitted a new appraisal of the situation to the Supreme Command; a reply to this was dispatched on December 3.

Attempts were made inside the pocket to build up the strongest possible defense line in the northwest, south, and west. In the Karpovka valley there were villages and farms, i.e., potential strongpoints. Otherwise the defense groups lay without cover on the low rises in the steppe. The weather was damp and drizzly.

Paulus's day
In the bunker that he is permitted to occupy alone, Paulus sleeps until the early-morning messages start arriving. He then goes over to the office bunker of General Schmidt, his chief of staff, whom he finds telephoning, organizing, and encouraging. Here he follows what is happening. Stocks of rations are redistributed. Paulus signs some documents. Some staff officers arrive to report. In the afternoon Paulus drives in an armored observation car, alternating with his chief of staff, to the forward headquarters of the various corps. On his return he takes a moment's rest. He then receives visitors, petitioners. He is available for con-

sultation with a general. He waits for the evening reports. After the evening reports there are exchanges of radio and teletype messages with positions outside the pocket, as far as these are possible. Paulus is waiting for events on the outside, at least he is expecting directions. The whole staff waits until long after midnight. By the time the early-morning reports start coming in, the staff officers, and soon after that Paulus, must be awake again.

Sunday, November 29, 1942

For the first time since the pocket was formed, the Army chaplains are performing their duties in proper surroundings. The enemy has ceased attacking. In the eastern part of the pocket front the soldiers are occupying their cunningly built positions. Naturally they have some salvaged stocks not possessed by the groups lying on the flat steppe in the west, south, and northwest.

Monday, November 30, 1942

The Army command has today decided to form Army reserves. Heavy weapons and a great deal of equipment, especially that of the 14th Panzer Division, have been lost. Hence the remaining soldiers, reinforced by supply sections, are to be formed into infantry units. For the time being the reserve is to be called the "Ludwig" Tank Grenadier Regiment. The weather is clear but cold. Since October 25, gradual improvement in air-supply system. Air Force General Fiebig has been appointed commissariat officer for air supplies.

That day the Russian High Command decided to leave the pocket more or less as it was, and, instead, to direct operations toward driving those German troops occupying positions behind the Don and the Chir farther away from the pocket.

Tuesday, December 1, 1942

North of O. the enemy succeeded in breaking through. That day the first combat groups composed of specialists (but no longer active in their special fields) can be paraded before the senior commanding officers. These specialist groups include a paratrooper contingent that has been sent to Stalingrad so that, in case of a victory, as many troop categories as possible were to be represented.

Acting on instructions, special efforts were being made on all fronts of the pocket to save ammunition.

Intermittent blizzards. Air traffic therefore restricted. Some planes land in Stalingrad, however; on the return flight they split up and land at various airfields as far away as Novocherkassk and Taganrog. The next day they have to be reassembled.

Wednesday, December 2, 1942

At the Bassargino airfield, inside the pocket, Antiaircraft Colonel Rosenfeld, the former police boxer, has assumed command.

All those troop sections in the pocket that have time are either drilling or resting.

In Kotelnikovo, outside the pocket, relief units are mustering around Colonel General Hoth. At headquarters in East Prussia, staff officers and Hitler were engaged in Operation Mauve, the occupation of the rest of France.

The 6th Army reported that with its reduced rations it could carry on for another twelve to sixteen days.

Lieutenant Colonel (Reserve) Werth:

The training of a group of Rumanians (about forty men) is making visible progress. The position here in the northeast corner of the pocket appears adequately equipped. Every morning the lieutenant colonel's orderly sweeps out his officer's wooden bunker with a broom provided for the purpose; in addition, all the lieutenant colonel's clothes are cleaned and brushed while the officer washes in a little tub. In this way the danger of infestation is averted. The officer was able to salvage a bag of sunflower seeds from the previous summer. After a snack (including herbs found in the area and pieces of bark brought in by soldiers), the lieutenant colonel goes over to the Rumanians' quarters. Combat practice is taking place in a hollow that the enemy cannot observe from the opposite bank of the Volga. Some soldiers—workmen in civilian life—are completing the interior furnishings of the two bunker rooms occupied by the lieutenant colonel. When the officer's battalion is to be sent in combat strength to the northern barrier position at the beginning of December, he immediately drives to the divisional commander and remonstrates. That same night he drives to the commander in the northern barrier position who had demanded his battalion and talks him out of precipitately engaging the Werth battalion. The following day it was late before he could again devote himself to his Rumanians. But the fatiguing journey had been worth while: the battalion remained in its accustomed routine in the northeast corner.

Thursday, December 3, 1942

Maximum centralization in the pocket in matters concerning rations, lumber, ammunition, fuel. Conservation commissions and inspections crisscross the pocket.

What have the Russians attacking in the northwest in mind? They are somewhat stronger than they were the previous day. General Paulus assumes that a last effort is being made here to create confusion in the pocket before the attempts at relief are begun.

Friday, December 4, 1942

Fog and ice.

The soldiers of the 16th Panzer Division spend the whole day watching battles take place to the right of their sector after strong artillery preparation.

A restless night from December 4 to 5 at Army headquarters; once again Paulus got no sleep at all. The days exhaust him. Major General von W. turned up at Army headquarters. According to him, the Russians were being greatly overrated; in 1929 he had been an instructor of Russian officers at the military academy in Omsk: actually they were not enemies but students —if only one could talk to them! The atmosphere at headquarters was partly depressed, but also partly hopeful; the group centering around General Schmidt, chief of staff, took an optimistic view of the situation.

Saturday, December 5, 1942

Over Bassargino, inside the pocket, ceiling 300 feet, visibility three-quarters of a mile, frequent driving snowstorms, all landings blind.

The Strack combat group, mounted on personnel carriers, cleaned up a small enemy wedge near B. Captain D. ran for his life not far from S. Since 3 A.M. parts of Panzer Regiment 36 had been marching through the snow; difficult to get bearings; by 5.30 A.M. the divisional and regimental commanders are close to Line 115.4 to 126.1. However, with a visibility of roughly 200 yards any clear recognition of the enemy is illusory.

Sunday, December 6, 1942

The twenty-four tanks of Panzer Regiment 36, the actual Army reserve, supported by "Ludwig" and "Fox" groups, now finally attack the enemy at 6.15 A.M. During the night, damp cold turning toward morning to sharp frost. The very weather for frostbite.

General Paulus spends another sleepless night; nevertheless, at Army headquarters the generally optimistic appraisal of events still holds. This optimistic outlook is meant to spread down to the five corps staffs and on to the divisional and regimental staffs. Colonel Clausius, chief of staff of the LI Army Corps, had the radio messages of the higher Army staffs monitored. He considered these messages too optimistic. When the Army chief of staff found out that the LI Corps was monitoring his radio messages, he had the Army radio code altered. Lieutenant Colonel von Zitzewitz, the officer who had been sent to Stalingrad by

Chief of General Staff Zeitzler, submitted his radio messages to the Army chief of staff for scrutiny. Schmidt found them too pessimistic. He made changes in the messages. After consulting with the first general staff officer of the Army, Zitzewitz henceforth dispatched radio messages without submitting them to Schmidt.

Monday, December 7, 1942

In the northwest of the pocket the enemy is quiet again. The Army reserve remains blocked here until 1 P.M.; then it returns to the ravine two miles north of D., to the center of the pocket. Of twenty-four tanks, five are still intact.

Captain O.:

That Monday the Rumanian Count O. deserted his men. A few days longer and they might have killed him. Two officers followed O.; they belonged to families similar to the captain's. This group of three officers went marauding in the villages of G. and V. and along the road to Gumrak, coming from the north and heading steadily south. There were no military police posts here. The group managed to survive until the pocket was finished. For an officer of the Royal Rumanian Army the situation was grotesque. Captain O. would not have known what to say to accusations made by a German fellow officer. His family, quite rich, could be traced back to the thirteenth century. The captain was still waiting for the intervention of a higher justice that would put an end to his activities. He arrived home unscathed.

Tuesday, December 8, 1942

Fine snow, driven by a strong wind, over the pocket area. Over the Volga, dense, wet snow. On the Volga the Russians maintained a steamer ferry which took from five to eight hours to cross the river through the great ice floes. The old boat was equipped with wrought-iron fittings, its capacity was small. A Russian general was in command of loading priorities at the dock.

Wednesday, December 9, 1942

After leaving the Don bridgeheads and parking the guns at an assembly point in the pocket, an infantry company was formed from the artillerymen of Artillery Regiment 14. Toward noon on December 9, after an infantry indoctrination talk, strong Russian artillery fire was audible from the north. The soldiers hurriedly gulped down some soup. Weapons and ammunition were then immediately issued, plus a blanket, mess kit, and topcoat. After a long march, two hours' rest. Later the men were sent to attack; they lost their way in the driving snow. When daylight came they saw the superiority of the enemy.

For Army headquarters, a normal pocket day.

Near Kotelnikovo relief troops were waiting to be allocated. Further troops, due by the 10th, had not yet arrived. The 23rd Panzer Division tried to advance by marching across the wide steppe area west of Elista. Light snow covered the ground around Kotelnikovo. At 6 A.M. an attempt is made to start up all the tanks.

The commander of the relief forces, Colonel General Hoth, successful in everything else, wanted so badly to get through to Stalingrad that he stationed himself on the road to Kotelnikovo to hasten the movement of his delayed troops. When the drivers saw the dreaded colonel general standing on the highway, nothing went right. Hoth shouted; he ordered the commanders standing around him to get busy and make themselves useful. But not until Hoth decided to break off the inspection did the mired vehicles manage to disentangle themselves.

Thursday, December 10, 1942

During the night the Army reserve was sent into action again, this time near Dimitrovka. The tanks carried out a night attack. Unfortunately they began by emerging 500 yards too far to the east. This enabled the enemy to launch a counterattack. The burning tanks, both enemy and German, satisfactorily illuminated the combat area, with bodies, equipment, and tanks clearly distinguishable against the snow. At first light the German tanks could move back with considerable numbers of prisoners. Some engineers and infantry remained behind at the fighting line. About fifteen enemy tanks, together with Russian artillery and antitank guns deployed in the open, stood in a semicircle of three to five hundred yards around these remaining defenders. That day each regiment was allotted only three artillery shells, seven antitank gun shells, and twelve 20-mm. cannon shells.

At dusk the combat staffs could follow the noise of engines, especially sounds of tracks, on the enemy side along the entire northwest wall of the pocket.

The Army military police made seventy-four arrests. Six court-martial sentences were passed that day. On the whole, however, discipline was satisfactory considering the circumstances. The military penal code contained sufficient legal provision for the maintenance of the organization, e.g.:

Para.	62	Violation of military service in wartime.
"	64	Absence without leave.
"	69	Desertion.
"	77	Failure to report desertion.
"	80	Breach of confinement to barracks.
"	81	Self-mutilation.
"	83	Evasion of military service by false representation.
"	84	Violation of military service for reasons of fear.
"	85	Cowardice.
"	89	Threatening a superior.
"	91	Insulting a superior.
"	92	Disobedience.
"	94	Defiance of orders.
"	96	Insubordination.
"	99	Incitement.
"	101	Joint complaint.
"	102	Incitement to dissatisfaction.
"	102a	Undermining of discipline.
"	103	Mutiny.
"	104	Failure to report mutiny.
"	106	Military insurrection (of more than three soldiers).
"	137	Damage to military property.
"	141	Dereliction of duty while on active service.
"	147	Other actions counter to military order.

In addition there were the general clauses of the National Socialist legislation.

Friday, December 11, 1942

Russian units, especially tanks, are moving past the south wall of the pocket toward the southwest (River A., town of Kotelnikovo); they can be observed with ease.

Army headquarters is expecting to receive favorable news for the following day.

Hitler, Zeitzler, Field Marshal von Manstein, the commandants in the pocket, as well as Colonel General Hoth and the relief troops under him, are waiting for the next day, when the relief attack is to take place.

Kunowski, quartermaster of the pocket, was negotiating near Gumrak with the quartermaster of the 2nd Air Corps. Serious thought was given to the problem of how to release a sufficient number of available planes for transporting supplies. A switch to supply flour by air instead of bread was also discussed. However, the attempt failed later since it was impossible to supply the quantity of bread required to span the gap of three or four days until bread could be baked by the Army.

Lieutenant General Pfeffer flew out of the pocket with his staff. His job was to round up the thousand men returning daily from leave and form them into combat groups outside the pocket. He was also to take possession of the stocks of fuel, ammunition, and rations belonging to the Army but outside the pocket. However, the Army Group had got there first. How was Pfeffer to address Field Marshal von Manstein? I respectfully request, etc. With this form he was unable to repossess the stocks belonging to the Army.

Saturday, December 12, 1942

First day of the relief thrust. Good clear weather.

Chain of command for the relief:

> Hitler
> Zeitzler
> von Manstein
> Hoth
> Kirchner
> Raus
> Hünersdorff in command of one intact regiment.

Army radio headquarters technicians in the pocket had managed to establish short-wave telephone connection with the outside. Starting at 9 P.M., conversations now took place between Army headquarters in the pocket and Army Group headquarters. The senior officers spoke first, beginning with General Paulus, then the lower-ranking officers, finally the highest-ranking in each branch. Field Marshal von Manstein would have liked to abolish this connection, since it held him up during crucial hours with what were sometimes emotional conversations; but he did not dare take steps in this direction. The first conversation took place between the Army communications command, Colonel Arnold, and the Army Group communications commandant, Colonel Müller. Colonel Müller then brought the field marshal to the phone while Colonel Arnold went to fetch General Paulus. The whole business sprang from purely technical initiative.

Hitler supervised Zeitzler, Zeitzler supervised Field Marshal von Manstein, von Manstein supervised Colonel General Hoth, Hoth supervised General of the Panzer Forces Friedrich Kirchner, Kirchner supervised Major General Raus, Raus supervised Colonel Hünersdorff. The latter supervised his regiment.

After the tanks had gained the bridgehead at K., ought they to have gone through at once to the vicinity of Stalingrad?

In the opinion of the second, fourth, and top-ranking commanders, yes. The tanks encountered hardly any resistance during the first two days.

What did the tanks do instead?

They took up a position in the village of Verkhne Kumskiy and waited for the enemy. As if at a tournament, they emerged from the village and beat the superior tank enemy.

What happened then?

The enemy brought up reinforcements. By the seventh relief day the Germans had worked into a routine. Now they might have been victorious. However, out of consideration for other fronts time had run out.

What was the mistake?

Overemphasis on the task of destruction. Had they been ordered to go all the way through, the tanks might have reached Stalingrad.

The attack began at 5.20 A.M. The penetration of the Russian front near Kotelnikovo was easy; the 200 tanks of the Panzer regiment simply drove through.

The day yielded captured equipment: five tanks, ten cannon, ten antitank guns, one multiple rocket launcher, five armored cars, many hand weapons, and 450 prisoners. In the evening, the usual picture. Fires in almost every direction, quivering flares; firing until late at night to drive away the sense of insecurity. After the evening reports, disappointment spread through the staffs. Hünersdorff said to Raus: "Either there were only weak forces opposing the division, in which case quite different plans could have been made, or the Russians managed to elude us."

Sunday, December 13, 1942
Second day of the relief thrust. Considerable fog patches, strong wind.

No church service. At the bend in the railway, a mile and a half west of the siding at Biryukovskiy, brief exchange of fire with enemy tanks. At S. the bridge over the River A. unfortunately collapsed under Hünersdorff's own tank. Due to the destruction of the bridge at S., the advance came to an end at noon that day. Colonel Hünersdorff, who had been pressing forward with such haste and who had caused the accident with his tank, was particularly annoyed at the injustice of this mishap.

Hitler, Zeitzler, von Manstein, Hoth, Kirchner, Raus, and finally Hünersdorff himself were waiting for rapid successes.

In the evening Paulus sent several messages to the Army Group, inquiring about successes.

Air Force General von Richthofen's comment on the attack of the relief army, after he had made an on-the-spot inspection, was: "There is no feeling of dashing forward, of a dramatic surge toward Stalingrad. They were 'fighting around' against an enemy they considered weak. Commanding general [Kirchner] kept only superficially informed of precarious situation in Stalingrad, hence not deeply enough concerned about his task." Among Army officers, von Richthofen was considered unjust in his pronouncements.

Monday, December 14, 1942
Third day of the relief thrust. Very bad weather, fog, fine rain, warm.

The relief group's task for the 14th read as follows: Hold bridgehead at S., reconnoiter toward G. and S., and obtain information on roads leading west and east. Panzer Regiment 11 left the bridgehead toward the neighboring village of Verkhne Kumskiy for a tank battle in the Kalmuck steppe.

On the 12th the fifth-ranking commander would have preferred the direction via Krugelyakov; it was closer and better suited to tanks. On the 13th the sixth-ranking commander took a different view from that of the officer immediately carrying out the orders (Hünersdorff). The latter was sometimes supported by the fourth-ranking commander (Hoth); serious differences of opinion at times existed between the fourth- and fifth-ranking commanders. The third-ranking commander did not concern himself with details; all he wanted was to see results. The second-ranking commander (Zeitzler) inquired twice a day about successes. The top commander (Hitler) waited impatiently for a resounding success.

Did any of those involved believe sufficiently in the success of the enterprise?

Since the disastrous blow to the Stalingrad Army, doubt extended over all movements as to whether they were not basically unfeasible. Considering the difficulty of every military transaction (icing of ravines, damage, friction, the enemy), it seemed at first impossible to advance even a single mile.

Placing four cannon in position:

A. Directives
B. Work to be done

I. Reconnaissance	Sequence	Time
(a) for	1.	
gun personnel	Orientation of terrain, reconnaissance of firing positions, command, and observation posts	done
	2.	
	Locating reserve positions for firing positions	done
	3.	
	Final reconnaissance and marking approach routes	. . . 1942
	4.	
	Organizing observation	done (will be carried out within each battery alternating every two days)
	5.	
	Preparing sketches with targets marked	not required until . . . 1942
	6.	
	Determining distances for probable target areas (repeated checks)	done

	7. Induction of platoon leaders, observation officers, and expendable noncommissioned officers	done
	8. Induction of gun crews	. . . 1942
	9. Exchange of observation results with other arms	every Tuesday and Friday, 1800 hrs. at battalion headquarters
	10. Setting up firing plan	on instructions of battalion commander
(b) for sections of detachment stationed at rear	1. Reconnaissance of reserve positions in agreement with commander of 2nd Batt. Infantry Regiment	done
	2. Determining sequence	done

II. Entrenching

1. for gun personnel and staff	(a) Digging in and roofing over guns, commanders' vehicles, and armored ammunition vehicles	by . . . 1942
	(b) Excavating command and observation posts	. . .
	(c) Preparing ammunition pits	at latest by
2. for staff batteries and rear sections of combat batteries	(a) Excavating fire trenches for fuel stocks	. . . 1942
	(b) Digging foxholes	. . .

(c)

Camouflaging vehicles   final

night

(signed): **H.**

Distribution:

Infantry Regiment	1
1st Batt. Infantry Regiment	1
2nd Batt. Infantry Regiment	1
Chief of Staff 1	5
Chief of Staff 3	5
Chief of Staff 2 (for information)	1
Chief of Staff Battery	1
Staff	2
Reserve	3
	20

Tuesday, December 15, 1942
Fourth day of the relief thrust. Ground fog.

Early in the morning tanks had to be towed across the bridge over the River A. due to icy conditions. The tanks again approached the village of Verkhne Kumskiy. The village, now occupied by the enemy, was taken under fire. When the ammunition was all used up, the tired tank drivers returned to their bridgehead in S. Because at 11 A.M. on the second day of the thrust the Panzer regiment had taken up its position in the village in question, the enemy was prompted to take up a similar position. Since the enemy was there, he was to be destroyed there. It was hoped that German losses would be considerably less than those of the enemy. The enemy hoped the same thing.

In the pocket, donations were being solicited for von Manstein. The collection yielded several hundred thousand reichsmarks, and this sum was to be offered to the field marshal at Christmas as an expression of thanks on the part of those caught in the pocket.

Wednesday, December 16, 1942
Fifth day of the relief thrust. Misty, partly foggy; overcast above the pocket.

Again the enemy was waiting early in the morning near the village of Verkhne Kumskiy. The relief Panzer Regiment 11, reinforced, prepared to do battle.

On the Army Group's northern flank, the enemy also attacked the front of the 8th Italian Army. One day later the front had ceased to exist there.

Thursday, December 17, 1942
Sixth day of the relief thrust. Sudden sharp frost.

The first general assault on Verkhne Kumskiy took place; the previous days' fighting had been tank battles. There was a delay of one hour in lining up for the attack on Verkhne Kumskiy. The attack on the enemy waiting encamped near the village miscarried.

Medical headquarters in the pocket reported the first case of death due to exhaustion; the report found its way via the Army Group to the Army Medical Corps administration in Berlin, with a copy to the Führer's headquarters.

Radio message from the 6th Army to Air Fleet 4: "Despite perfect weather and brilliant sunshine, not a single plane landed on December 17. The Army would appreciate an explanation as to why no planes are being flown.—Schmidt."

Considerable enemy aerial activity.

Enemy vehicles and guns were moved past the pocket front toward the south.

Paulus's Army orders, after consultation with Schmidt: No officer was to be taken prisoner alive. However, it was forbidden to shoot oneself first.

Friday, December 18, 1942
Seventh day of the relief thrust. Sharp frost, clear.

The second general assault on the village of Verkhne Kumskiy was also unsuccessful. Radio silent on all movements of the relief corps.

At noon the Italian Foreign Minister Count Ciano, and the Chief of the Comando Supremo, Marshal Count C., arrived at Wolfsschanze, somewhat exhausted from the journey north; they were received by Deichmann, von Waldenburg, Ribbentrop, Göring, Zeitzler, Keitel, Jodl, and Hitler. The subject of the discussions was the critical situation in the southern section of the eastern front. Count Ciano and Count C. did not permit the disaster to the Italian Army to affect their exemplary attitude. However, they wondered whether it might not be possible to come to an arrangement with Russia. Hitler rejected the idea. On this and the following day he was entirely occupied with the discussions; even Zeitzler could not reach him.

Von Manstein dispatched an officer, Major Eismann, to the pocket, where he was to speak for von Manstein. In discussion with the much lower-ranking major, General Schmidt (remembering the Hentsch case in World War I) refused to countenance the idea of a panic solution. He said: "Colonel General Hoth has advanced beyond all expectation. When he is within some twenty miles of us we will break out in order to make the last few miles easier for him." Colonel General Paulus said: "We must avoid any excitement among the troops in the present situation."

Saturday, December 19, 1942
Eighth day of the relief thrust.

The enemy withdrew from Verkhne Kumskiy. Hünersdorff pursued him; Hünersdorff did not even halt his tanks during the night. During the latter part of the night he approached to within roughly thirty-five miles of the pocket, near V. on the Myschkova.

Some hundred tanks of the 6th Army were waiting in the southwest corner of the pocket. It was said they had enough fuel for twenty miles.

At noon Field Marshal von Manstein requested permission from Zeitzler for the 6th Army to break out. At 6 P.M. von Manstein gave orders to the encircled Army: "Winter thunderstorm as soon as possible," i.e., the tanks of the 6th Army were to go to meet the relief corps. The Army did not carry out the order. Von Manstein said: "In different circumstances I would relieve a recalcitrant Army commander; but at the present moment this does not appear feasible, nor would Hitler wish it."

A Rumanian squadron of platoon strength, deployed in the R. sector, disappeared. The men scrounged food in the hinterland. Other Rumanian units proved to be reliable ammunition carriers and sentries. More important was the fact that some of them brought horses with them.

Sunday, December 20, 1942
Ninth day of the relief thrust.

Hitler returned to the question of the Stalingrad pocket. He now decided the pocket should not be given up after all.

Monday, December 21, 1942
Tenth day of the relief thrust.

Bridgehead at V. being held.
Radio message: Junction imminent.
Radio message: See you soon.

Tuesday, December 22, 1942
Eleventh day of the relief thrust.

All attacks on V. repulsed. General Kirchner and Major General Raus met near the riverbank. Without new reinforcements it would be difficult to get out of V. and closer to Stalingrad in this section.

Calculation:

From bases K. to K. 33 miles
From bases K. to S. 45 miles
From bases S. to V. 48 miles

From base V. to the heights east of Zety it would have been another 23 miles. From there 22 miles to Rokotino (beginning of the pocket).

The Army Group indicated, but did not give orders: Panzer wedges will force a corridor from outside and inside through the Russian encirclement, the 6th Army will then leave its positions in Stalingrad and, after receiving supplies of gasoline, ammunition, and food, will flow through the corridor toward the southwest. The northern front of Stalingrad will re-form and withdraw fighting, section by section, in the following order: 60th Motorized Infantry Division, parts of the 16th Panzer Division, and the 24th Panzer Division.

Twenty-six trucks under Captain Prüm were waiting near V. with spare parts, fuel, and rations. They were to drive through the first gap made in the pocket.

Loss of radiotelephone contact

On the 18th a marriage by proxy was performed by short-wave radio. On December 20 the transmitting station on the Chir was threatened by the enemy. On the 21st the transmitting mast was shot down. When it was rebuilt at a more distant point, it was impossible to establish contact. The Army Group (actually not very perturbed about the cessation of telephone contact) offered to fly in a Sawfish radioteletype machine with coding attachment and tape transmitter. The apparatus was to be flown in in mid-January in two four-motored planes. The 6th Army declined the offer.

Wednesday, December 23, 1942
Twelfth day of the relief thrust.

The day when the 6th Panzer Division had to part company
with the relief forces of V. In the open northern flank of the Army
Group the Russians were already halfway along the route to
Rostov. Had they reached Rostov, two Army Groups would have
been surrounded.

Would the relief thrust have been successful if it had been
begun on December 4 rather than December 12?

Yes.

All divisions in the pocket have handed over their vehicles at
a central assembly point. Letters six feet high were painted on
the vehicles' sides in white paint. The maneuvering of the mass
of vehicles into and out of the pocket was to proceed on routes
marked with little flags; a regimental commander of the smoke-
screen detachment was to supervise and protect the anticipated
one-way traffic with his unit. Planes would drop fifty-five-gallon
drums of gasoline from their side doors near the access route.
Plans were to set up a temporary airfield halfway between the
breakout point and Kotelnikovo.

Thursday, December 24, 1942

A sunny day, but very cold; during the morning First Lieutenant
Knörzer and his engineers were able to clean up an enemy breakthrough. Thin layer of snow. Everything very quiet; at various
points in the south and west of the pocket, propaganda voices
from Russian loudspeakers:

> Oh come, all ye faithful
> And listen to my voice!
> The truth I bring from Heaven
> To ye who have the choice.
>
> The day is now approaching
> When Hitler's state is past—
> Oh happy man whose life
> Till that great day shall last!

The Russian soldiers, volunteers, did not speak German; they had learned the words by heart phonetically. In spite of intensified propaganda that day, there were no German defectors.

General Paulus issued an order of the day. In the south of the pocket, the tanks of the Army reserve were now no longer required. They were transferred to the north, the location of their original divisions. As soon as it began to get dark, i.e., after 3 P.M. (General Paulus had not yet returned from his daily inspection of the command posts up front), the Christmas spirit started to spread in the pocket. Special rations were distributed. All the chaplains were kept busy.

Captain H., 305th Division, reports: Children's Christmas carols were sung, everyone was a child again, it was Christmas.

General Staff Major W., staff of the II Army Corps: I recall how the general summoned us, that's to say, sent a message requesting our company at such-and-such a time in his quarters, it was in the afternoon, and I remember General von Seydlitz shook hands all round and gave everyone a slice of bread as a Christmas present.

Lieutenant Colonel B., 389th Division: We had huge stocks of iron and steel as well as copper, brass, and aluminum, and from these I had my armorer and his assistant make Christmas gifts—letter openers, ash trays, picture frames, etc. Even drew some designs myself, such as little stars from copper sheeting, with a hole punched at one point so we could hang them on our Christmas tree. I had also designed the little Christmas tree. Its four sections had been sawn out of plywood and could be fastened together.

First Lieutenant W., 60th Motorized Division: My fellow officers had created a Christmas atmosphere in a big tent with candles. A large table had been set up, and on it lay loaves of bread and chocolate. I read out the Army order of the day from Colonel General Paulus as follows: All of us, from the oldest general to the youngest soldier, are standing shoulder to shoulder and form a sworn fellowship against which all attacks will founder.

We will hold the fortress of Stalingrad until the relief sent by the Führer smashes the ring encircling us. After that I distributed among the men some Iron Crosses First and Second Class that we had received from the division. "Silent Night, Holy Night" brought the celebration to an end.

Captain von F.: On Christmas Eve an advanced grenade-throwing platoon, in two shifts, listened to a Christmas record of the Dresden Church of the Cross choir on the divisional chaplain's portable phonograph.

Colonel F.: So I had picture frames and copper letter openers made for the regimental commander, the battalion medical officer, and my company commander. My adjutant, a grade-school teacher, drew Christmas cards to go with them. The weather was quite seasonable, with plenty of snow and frost. From what was still available in rations I made up the following menus for the Christmas holidays:

Dec. 24, 1942: LUNCH: barley with horse meat.
SUPPER: 9 oz. bread, 3 oz. sausage, 1 oz. butter, real coffee.
EXTRA RATIONS: horse meat stew, 3 oz. bread, 3 oz. chocolate, 1 oz. candies. 10 oz. rum and 2½ bouillon cubes.
SMOKES: 10 cigarettes and 1 cigar.
Dec. 25, 1942: LUNCH: pea soup and horse meat.
SUPPER: 6 oz. bread, 3 oz. sausage, 1 oz. butter, coffee.
EXTRA RATIONS: 6 oz. bread, 1½ oz. cornstarch pudding and jam, 1½ oz. chocolate, and 12 oz. rum.
SMOKES: 2 cigars.
Dec. 26, 1942: LUNCH: rice with horse meat.
SUPPER: 6 oz. bread, 2 horse meat rissoles, 1 oz. butter, coffee.
EXTRA RATIONS: 3 oz. bread, 1 oz. candies, 3 oz. chocolate.
SMOKES: 1 cigar and 2 cigarettes.

Von Manstein, outside the pocket, had now finally bogged down. Some of his divisions were retreating aimlessly. The Tatsinskaya airfield, which had been supplying Stalingrad, lost with 100 airplanes. The 6th Army was not to be told of these difficulties.

Teletypes—Christmas

General Schulz—General Schmidt
December 24, 1942, 1705 to 1715 hours.

Dear Schmidt,

The Field Marshal and all of us are thinking especially of the whole 6th Army this evening. There is not much news to give you today.

Fangohr is still fighting a defensive battle. Enemy seems to have moved up fresh reinforcements there. Nothing special on the Chir front. The 11th Panzer Division's attack from Morozovskaya toward the west has temporarily halted the enemy advance there. No decision yet about you from Supreme Command headquarters. The field marshal says to tell you to plan for the probable Thunderclap solution. We are waiting for better weather when we can fly in the required fuel and rations with all available . . . [gap in original]. What do you still have?

Schmidt . . . Are the planes still sure of taking off in spite of the threat to Tatsinskaya?

Schulz . . . Take-off still assured and emergency airfields set up.

Schmidt . . . Will Fangohr be able to hold the Myschkova sector?

Schulz . . . We very much hope so. However, there is a chance he may have to narrow down the present bridgehead.

Schmidt . . . Has one of Fangohr's Panzer divisions been withdrawn to the west bank of the Don?

Schulz . . . One Panzer division had to be moved westward across the Don for the protection of Morozovskaya. Tomorrow, however, the "Viking" S.S. Division will be arriving in the Salsk area by rail and cross-country march from the south. Furthermore, we have again demanded urgent and sizable reinforcement from the Army Group. The decision of Supreme Command headquarters is still awaited on this. No more news. The Supreme Commander and I heartily reciprocate your Christmas greetings.

Friday, December 25, 1942

Whirling, driving snow since early morning. Men were to be taken that morning from the northern barrier position to a special

Christmas service near Gorodische. They had to return hurriedly.
When they got back to their position, they saw that the Russians
were already occupying it. The rest of the day and during the
night they lay in improvised snow hollows. Later they were
wiped out.

The Army command regarded the Russian attack on the northern front as the beginning of the major offensive.

Logic: just because most of the riflemen are dead, the gun crew
at Point 139.7 holds out and in short order destroys thirteen
enemy tanks.

Atmosphere at Führer's headquarters: busy working on important orders, but these were not concerned with Stalingrad. That
day, as on December 18, 19, 21, 22, 23, and 24, Zeitzler was
unable to see Hitler.

Atmosphere at Army Group headquarters: the 6th Army is now
lost. Nothing more can be done for it other than to tell it the
truth. But no one had the courage to do this.

Atmosphere at Army staff headquarters: some of the troops
needed feeding up if they were to undertake long marches and
assault actions without many of them dropping out.

That afternoon the commanding generals of the 6th Army each
had a private interview with Paulus and Schmidt. During von
Seydlitz's visit, Paulus referred to his reports to headquarters and
the resultant measures taken; von Seydlitz interrupted Paulus. He
explained again why he had been obliged to act independently in
the days immediately following the encirclement; he rejected once
and for all the accusations of arbitrary action made against him
by envious persons and superior officers.

None of the commanding generals had any advice to give. At
each interview there was discussion as to whether the troops should
be advised of the situation, i.e., alarmed, or remain ignorant, i.e.,
reassured. Seydlitz was in favor of advising them. Paulus tried to
compromise: Could the question perhaps be dealt with individually?
Schmidt said one ought not to add to the physical strain of the
ordinary man by burdening him with mental worries.

Saturday, December 26, 1942

That day the bread ration was reduced to 1¾ ounces per head per day. According to the calculations of the Army general staff, this order should have been given on December 23; however, if given at that time it would have destroyed the Christmas spirit desired for the next few days.

The Army prisoner-of-war camp was situated not far from V.; by the end of December it contained 3,500 Russians. Paulus gave orders to transport the prisoners to the western part of the pocket. His reasoning was that there the Russians would liberate the prisoners the quickest; later he ordered that the prisoners be handed over to the Russians, but this order was not carried out. Prisoners had never been given back to a numerically superior enemy.

During the afternoon the Supreme Commander of the 6th Army sent the following message concerning the Army's position to the Supreme Command of the Army Group for transmission to Supreme Command headquarters:

Severe losses, cold, and insufficient rations have now seriously reduced the fighting strength of the divisions. I therefore have to report:
1. For a limited time the Army will be able to continue to deal with minor enemy attacks and local crises. However, this cannot be done unless improved supplies and relief are flown in without delay.
2. If Russians withdraw strong forces facing Hoth and with these or other troops proceed to undertake mass attacks on fortress, the latter will not be able to hold out for long.
3. Breakout no longer feasible unless corridor created first and Army reinforced with men and supplies.

I therefore petition that highest authority be requested to take forceful measures for the speedy relief of the Army, if the over-all situation does not compel the sacrifice of the Army.

Needless to say, the Army will do everything in its power to hold out as long as possible.

Evening bulletin:

"Today only 70 tons flown in. Bread finished tomorrow, fat

tonight, in some units no evening rations tomorrow. Stringent measures now imperative."

Confidential directive:
   A central office issued the confidential directive that no wounded soldier or other person flown out of the pocket was to be transported west of the Dnieper line, in order to prevent a flow of uncontrolled news from the pocket reaching the Reich or the occupied territories.

Saturday, December 27, 1942
   Quiet enough to hold field church services.
   Lieutenant L. flew into the pocket from an office outside the pocket to audit a supplies account. A military police unit assigned him to a fortress battalion. The fortress battalion was trained in the use of carbines and sent north. Their job there was to uncover foxholes and remove dead comrades.
   Supply Regiment 16 dissolved. Divisional Supply Office 16 reassigned one noncommissioned officer and eleven men as infantrymen:
   Sergeant Hellekemper.
   Corporal Ehelebe returned to Divisional Supply Office on January 20 with slight frostbite of fingers of left hand.
   Corporal Gundermann returned to Divisional Supply Office on January 19 with slight splinter head wound.
   Corporal Meis reported at a field hospital on January 14, bullet wound in left forearm.
   Corporal Schlabach back at Divisional Supply Office on January 21 with slight frostbite of right foot as well as frost damage to hands.
   Corporal Wolters back at Divisional Supply Office on January 19 with two light flesh wounds.
   Corporal Blech returned to Divisional Supply Office on January 19.
   Corporal Drissen killed on January 16 at Orlovka.

Corporal Schneider dead.

Private First Class Krichen reported to the unit medical officer on January 13 with sprained foot.

Corporal Mehlmann flown out of the pocket on January 23 with bullet wound in arm.

Private First Class Büscher dead.

General Hube made a telephone survey in the pocket. The question: Which is preferable—to abandon the pocket and break out immediately, or to hold the pocket? He was supposed to fly to Hitler two days later.

Pathologist H.:

The Supreme Command dispatched the prominent Berlin pathologist and anatomist H. to the pocket with confidential instructions to determine by autopsies why soldiers not engaged in combat were dying. After landing, the pathologist encountered some animosity on the part of the doctors in the pocket whom he had known before; some of them had trained under him. H. tried not to seem like an inspector. Corpses were thawed out and dissected. H. found: under the skin and around the internal organs hardly a scrap of fatty tissue; in the viscera a watery, gelatinous mass, the organs livid; instead of red and yellow bone marrow, a transparent, quaking, jelly-like substance, liver congested, heart small and brown, right heart chamber and right auricle markedly enlarged. Colonel D., the medical officer accompanying H., said: senescent bodies. H. remained for the duration of the pocket in Stalingrad and was then taken prisoner with his colleagues.

That day Paulus conveyed a Croatian decoration to von Seydlitz. Von Seydlitz did not wish to accept the decoration; under the circumstances he considered it unsuitable. He was awarded the decoration by the authorities in Croatia, the Croatian regiment in the pocket being under von Seydlitz's corps command.

Tuesday, December 29, 1942

Chief of General Staff of the Army Zeitzler put himself and his immediate colleagues on pocket rations. After a few days, productivity suffered. Hitler was not convinced by the experiment because he was counting on unofficial supplies being available to the divisions in the pocket.

First Lieutenant G. died, inactive, in central Stalingrad following a jaw injury.

First Lieutenant G.'s hunting record since the crossing of the Don: Day X + 8: G. shot the two children first, then the woman, then the commissar. Day X + 21: smoking out a bunker line; first, shoot into the gunports to make a broad opening; then flame throwers, blocking off chances of escape. Day X + 30: dumping hand grenades and gasoline into an obstinate cellar. Day X + 31: G.'s column breaks through, twelve men fall at 100 yards, ten at fifty. The remainder reach the enemy position and stab the enemy to death. Day X + 43: seizing food supplies and valuable articles in a guerrilla area. Goods to the value of 50,000 marks are secured in the villages and farms. Fighting a stubborn enemy required flexibility. The inactivity of Stalingrad was not for G.

General Hube's mission

Hube left the pocket at noon. He was fully prepared to make Hitler sit up and listen. A thorough questioning of all chiefs of staff and commanders in the pocket proved that he had their backing; he carried outspoken letters with him. Paulus had impressed upon him the necessity of speaking his mind. In this mood the soldier came to the totally different atmosphere of the Army Group headquarters in Taganrog, an atmosphere devoted to a higher level of thinking. Von Manstein confided his own far-reaching plans to him: all that was necessary, he said, was to proceed skillfully and relieve Hitler of the supreme command. Hube fell in with these ideas too. At Wolfsschanze he was first wined and dined by friends. He was accustomed to talk freely among friends. He told them about von Manstein and about the pocket. In these austere but totally un-pocketlike surroundings, much of his tension was siphoned off; idle among men unremittingly occupied, his appetite satisfied, he found it hard to keep to his instructions. Hitler appeared, he was optimistic. He asked Hube to have dinner with him. Hitler said: "A reorganization of air supplies is actually quite feasible." The "Bodyguard," "Death's Head," and "Reich" divisions of the S.S. would soon, he went on, be ready; by mid-February they would be in position around Charkov. What made Hube's situation especially difficult was the fact that at the time it was quite impossible for the 6th Army to break out; further-more, a fresh relief attempt was not feasible at that moment. This meant that his mission was on the one hand too late and on the other premature. Hitler awarded him a decoration. After his reception by Hitler, Hube inspected airfields and supply measures outside the pocket. Meanwhile, he had become sympathetically inclined toward the attitude outside the pocket. In an optimistic mood he flew back on January 8 and reported to Paulus. It was only against the background of life in the pocket, which he re-entered after flying over the ring of fire around Stalingrad, visible in the night as far as the eye could see, that the results of his journey seemed to him meager. On January 20, at Hitler's express orders, Hube was flown out of the pocket. In later years Hube never again let a change of atmosphere deflect him from a fixed purpose.

Wednesday, December 30, 1942

Ambulance drivers brought the rumor from Gumrak that Paulus had been in Wolfsschanze. The next rumor was that von Manstein was coming to the pocket over the New Year. The Army Command dispatched Major Toepke to the Army Group. Paulus said to Toepke: "I wish to know exactly what increase in air supplies we can reckon with from now on." Fresh, in excellent health, Schmidt, Chief of the General Staff of the 6th Army, told Toepke: "See to it that out there they stop blasting useless holes opposite the Tatsinskaya front. The Army is looking to you now." The Ia of the Army told Toepke that, since any large-scale action was evidently no longer possible now, the troops must be given freedom of movement; groups must split up in all directions, each with a radio set, pack, change of underwear, mess kit, and kindling. This must all be prepared.

So Toepke flew out of the pocket. Outside, an immediate change of atmosphere; here the pocket could no longer be visualized. Colonel B. of the General Staff said to Toepke: "One can't uproot trees with one's bare hands."

Major Toepke's mission

Toepke was received by Field Marshal von Manstein, who was pressed for time. "Go and see Air Force General Fiebig tomorrow," he said. The next day Fiebig was in Salk, flying weather being favorable there. Fiebig's adjutant sent Toepke to General V. The latter sent him to von Manstein's chief of staff, Major General Schulz, who was working on a complicated survey of the Panzer situation; he sent Toepke to his deputy. The following morning Toepke reported with this deputy to the commander of the Luftwaffe, von Richthofen. The latter held a long and intensive conversation with Major Toepke. In rank, von Richthofen occupied a position one step below Field Marshal von Manstein. In this capacity he ordered cooperation on the part of all those involved; he tried to telephone both Berlin and Wolfsschanze. Static interference prevented both calls from getting through. The next day, the fourth outside the pocket, Major Toepke again called on the Army Group and spoke to the officer in charge of supplies, General von Fiedler. The latter was a member of the group that secretly opposed Hitler. Von Fiedler tried to steer Major Toepke toward this group. The conversation cost him the afternoon and evening. Anyway, von Fiedler could do nothing about the situation in Stalingrad. Major Toepke looked for a billet near the Salk airfield. He would not have been received by still higher staffs (actually the only remaining one would have been Wolfsschanze). If he did not want to get a reputation for having a pocket complex, he would have to restrain the intensity of his requests. If he did this, he might not be successful. Toepke got into radio contact with Kunowski, his superior in the pocket. He was prepared to risk everything the following day, i.e., to disregard all military formality. However, the Army Group responded to him with a sympathy that forgave even a lapse of this kind.

Thursday, December 31, 1942

Hitler emphasized his intention of sending an S.S. corps toward Stalingrad from the Charkov area at latest by the end of February. From Charkov to Stalingrad the distance was 325 miles; there were two rivers to be crossed.

We hope the war will soon be over, though it doesn't look much like an early final victory, etc., said Lieutenant General W. to Major General F. at the New Year's Eve celebrations of the "Proud" Division. Well, we need faith and hope to carry on, replied Major General Fiedler.

New Year's Eve, 1940, had been spent by the 6th Army on the Luxembourg frontier; tracer bullets were fired at midnight. New Year's Eve, 1941, the Army was at the River Mius; the day passed quietly. New Year's Eve, 1942, the Russians who had surrounded the Army fired a ring of tracer and artillery bullets into the night sky at exactly twelve midnight. General Paulus came out in surprise from his sleeping bunker.

Friday, January 1, 1943

During the day the Russians carried out powerful reconnaissance thrusts on the west, southwest, and northwest fronts of the pocket. Comrades Voronov and Rokossovski suspiciously observed the failure of almost all the thrusts. In the evening a German transport plane was shot down over the Russian positions. Staff officers found letters in the plane, among them one from Lieutenant General Edler von Daniels, indicating the disposition of the German defense forces. That day the 6th Army issued an order concerning the use of ammunition. At the regimental command level it was permitted to fire per day three rounds per light field howitzer, two rounds per antitank cannon, and two rounds per 88-mm. antitank cannon, and at corps command level one round per heavy field howitzer. Rifle ammunition was to be used sparingly. Any increase at focal points was subject to Army approval.

The cunning servants

A weak company of the Italian Eastern Army, motorized, was assigned to an elite unit, the Savoy regiment; these men had never had the desire to form part of an elite. In November they were sent to Stalingrad because the regiment needed lumber to furnish the officers' mess; remnants of lumber were to be found in the Stalingrad ruins. The Stalingrad pocket closed around the company that had been sent to Stalingrad. Since the company possessed neither papers nor written orders to support its presence in Stalingrad, its commanding officer failed to provide it with a status that would entitle it to rations. Moreover, the company was afraid that assignment of rations would mean assignment to combat. The Italian officers who had sent the company on this lumber detail regarded the unit as missing and did not dare report the illegal mission; soon after December 16 they fled to the west. The men, cavalrymen and auto mechanics, now reduced to forty, raided supply transports in the pocket. In January the men were rounded up by military police. A court-martial had them shot. They had previously tried to explain their special status in the pocket.

Saturday, January 2, 1943

Ground fog. During the preceding twenty-four hours no planes had been able to land in the pocket.

The Russian Generals Voronov and Rokossovski conceived the idea of presenting an ultimatum to the surrounded Army.

Sunday, January 3, 1943

The Army news bulletin issued in the pocket reports:

"The Udet fighter squadron, of which four planes are in the pocket, reports its 4,000th enemy plane shot down. Staff Medical Officer M. of the 14th Panzer Division has been transferred to

Berlin to become instructor at the military medical academy there and is being flown out. Training and instruction courses among the fortress battalions are proceeding."

Morale, limited opportunity for defection

Since the summer the 6th Army had been driving back Russian forces. A victorious army enjoys moral cohesion. This moral standard survived for a time; when the Army had ceased to function properly, then it gradually disintegrated. At this period, however, it was difficult to alter existing organizational conditions in the pocket. Group defection would have required complicity; but among those taken into confidence there might be a traitor. Single defection was no less dangerous; the fire of those left behind would have been concentrated on the individual. Hence the transfer to a different organizational form of the men already lost in Stalingrad was only possible if the officers ordered such a transfer or capitulation.

The Communist writer Weinert, who traveled around the pocket on the Russian side, conceived the plan of entering the pocket at night; he wished to appeal to General Paulus's conscience. Would the sentries listen to him? asked the Russian Colonel T. A section of the southern front could be used for the secret crossing. Perhaps Weinert should wear a German uniform? And then take it off at German headquarters? In 1912, in Warsaw, Rosa Luxemburg convinced a prison official that he should release her. In 1942 Weinert would probably have been handed over to a military court in the pocket before he could appeal to Paulus's chivalry. Would he have got through to Paulus? Would Paulus have been chivalrous? He was a Junker. That doesn't mean a thing, said Willi Bredel, he is in the pay of the bourgeois. No, replied Weinert, perhaps he does have chivalrous feelings. But are Junkers chivalrous? asked Colonel T. He advised against the plan.

Monday, January 4, 1943

Snow, strong east wind. All communications within the pocket hampered.

When members of the LI Army Corps looked out of their bunker in the morning, they could see a column of ten trucks not too far off. The officers were annoyed because the column, standing there in the snow, was bound to attract enemy fire toward the bunker. The trucks turned out to be ambulance trucks. The column had lost its way. Because the men were exhausted, they had driven no farther. Drivers, helpers, and wounded had frozen to death.

Private First Class H. had been marching from six in the morning in the western part of the pocket. At 5 P.M. his forearm was shot to pieces. With no sensation of pain he walked until about 10 P.M. to a dressing station. The doctor there tried to persuade him to have his arm amputated. The soldier no longer had his wits about him. He asked that his arm be spared. If he had said "amputate," he might have been flown out.

Expert assistance

Three Himalayan explorers known personally to Hitler arrived in Novocherkassk. They could have told which food and winter supplies should have priority in being flown in to Stalingrad. However, the requirements of the Army were inflexibly contained in

Confidential Command File Ia No.0874/42: 17 oz. bread, 3 oz. canned meat, 3½ oz. vegetables, 3 oz. supper rations, 2 oz. fat, 2 oz. sugar, 1 oz. spices and salt, ½ oz. beverage, 1 oz. smokes. Total: 2 lb. 1 oz. plus packing, 2 lb. 4 oz. For a total of 250,000 men: 282 tons per day.

Tuesday, January 5, 1943

Generals Voronov and Rokossovski presented Russian headquarters with the following draft text for an ultimatum to the 6th Army:

Since November 26, 1942, the 6th German Army, the units of the 4th Panzer Army, and attached reinforcement troops, have been completely encircled. The units of the Red Army, commanding powerful technical equipment and strong reserves, have surrounded the German Army Group with a tight ring. None of the hopes for the relief of your troops from the south and southwest have been fulfilled. The German troops hastening to your aid have been destroyed by the Red Army, the remnants of these troops are fleeing in the direction of Rostov. The German air-transport fleet, intended to supply you with a starvation minimum of food and fuel supplies, is being forced by the successful action of the Red Army to change airfields frequently and to fly into the pocket from great distances. The Red Army's air defense is causing it immense losses in aircraft and flying personnel.

You must bear in mind that here in the south the Supreme Command of the Red Army is carrying out an operation of enormous extent for which strong operative reserves and large quantities of war matériel have been brought up. The situation of your encircled troops is a grave one; they are suffering from hunger, sickness, and cold, although the severe Russian winter is only just beginning; severe frost, icy winds, and snowstorms lie ahead. Your soldiers are not equipped with the necessary winter clothing and are living under conditions extremely detrimental to their health.

You, Commander in Chief, know better than anyone else that there is no prospect whatever of your being relieved, that your situation is hopeless and further resistance pointless.

In the history of war there have been many examples of gifted army commanders who, on finding themselves with their brave troops in a hopeless situation of this kind, made the correct decision to avoid unnecessary bloodshed: to cease resistance, lay down their arms, and surrender. And history has never condemned them for this.

In view of your undeniably hopeless situation it is suggested that, in order to avoid useless bloodshed, you cease further resistance and accept the following terms of surrender:

The encircled German troops, headed by you and your staff, will cease resistance and surrender in an organized manner your arms, gear, and equipment in working order.

We guarantee all officers and men who cease resistance their lives and complete security, as well as—when the war is over—their return to Germany or any other country to which the prisoner-of-war may desire to go. All members of capitulating units will be permitted to keep their uniforms, rank insignia, decorations, personal property, articles of value, and senior officers their swords. All capitulating officers and men will immediately be issued normal rations. All sick and wounded, and soldiers suffering from frostbite, will receive medical aid.

Your reply in writing is expected on January . . . , 1943, 0000 hours, conveyed by a truce officer personally authorized by yourself who on January . . . between 1000 and 0000 hours will drive along the road to Bay 564 in an automobile bearing a white flag. We hereby inform you that, should you reject our offer of capitulation, the troops of the Red Army and the Red Air Fleet will continue with their overwhelming forces and resources completely to destroy the encircled German troops by inflicting blows of constantly increasing severity, for which you will bear full responsibility.

> Representative of Supreme Headquarters of the
> Red Army, Colonel General of the Artillery Voronov.
> Supreme Commander of the Don front,
> Lieutenant General Rokossovski.

Wednesday, January 6, 1943

Six Junkers 52's, private planes of Göring, Ribbentrop, Ley, etc., arrived from Wolfsschanze at the airfields serving Stalingrad.

Quartermaster in Chief K. organized super-express trains at the Army Group level; these trains were put together in Schleswig-Holstein and loaded with smoked sausage, bacon, Chocacola, and other food concentrates. The trains were given priority over all other trains, even ammunition transports; from Schleswig-Holstein they were able to reach Rostov in southern Russia in seven days.

The Russian general offensive against the pocket was scheduled for that day. Transportation delays developed. General Voronov telephoned the People's Commissar for Communications, Comrade Crulev, in Moscow. In spite of Comrade Stalin's misgivings, a four-day postponement of the date for the offensive was agreed upon.

Thursday, January 7, 1943

The ultimatum drafted by Comrade Voronov was approved, with some changes, by Moscow headquarters. General Voronov obtained a copy of the 1907 Hague Convention. Past experience was lacking. As laid down by the Hague Convention, four copies of the ultimatum were prepared, two copies each in Russian and

German. Generals Voronov and Rokossovski signed all four copies, of which two were handed over and two held in reserve. Following the terms of the Convention, two volunteers were summoned as truce officer and interpreter. Major S. and Captain D. were familiarized with the conditions of international law. The evening before the presentation, i.e., the evening of January 7, attempts were made to establish radio contact with the staff of the encircled Army. When there was no reply, the station, maintained by the Russian Don front to influence the surrounded troops, transmitted the message throughout the night that truce officers would be dispatched.

The 376th Infantry Division occupied a position at the western-most point of the pocket. The soldiers lay in snow holes; no field fortifications had been erected, although a partially burned village with remnants of lumber not far away could have been used. The Army decided to replace the 376th Infantry Division with sections of the 29th Motorized Infantry Division. Lower echelons of command suggested a simple exchange of the artillery of the two divisions, in which case the guns could have remained in position. This was rejected by Army Command, which claimed that, according to experience, troops preferred to handle their own equipment.

Friday, January 8, 1943

Volga frozen over. A continuous stream of Russian supplies poured across the river on several routes. The German artillery of Divisions 94, 389, 305, 79, 100, 295, 71 has been waiting a long time for such good targets; but they lack the ammunition necessary for disruptive action.

General Hube returned that day to the pocket. Owing to the optimism he radiated, some activity spread around him in the western part of the pocket.

Truce officers S. and D. left the trenches in the northern sector of the encirclement front and, as announced by the radio station, arrived at the enemy's wire barricade. There was no one to receive them. After a time the troops in the pocket opened fire with grenade throwers. General Voronov said: "So the enemy side is behaving like an enemy." From Moscow came the order: Negotiations are to be broken off.

During the night the replacement of the 376th Infantry Division by the 29th Motorized Infantry Division continued in the western tip. The motorized division was, so to speak, moving into a trap that the Russians intended to spring shut.

Saturday, January 9, 1943

Contrary to his instructions from Moscow, General Voronov decided to dispatch Comrades S. and D. once more, this time from the south side of the encirclement front. At the wire barricade the truce officers were received by German officers, who demanded that they present the document. S. protested; in accordance with international law, the truce officers were conducted through the German positions blindfold. The truce officers had brought large white cloths with them for this purpose. The emissaries handed over the envelope with the ultimatum to Paulus in person.

After consulting with higher authorities, Paulus refused to reply to the document.

Shortly before 11 P.M. the Russian command informed the German Army that the general offensive against the pocket would begin on the morning of January 10 at 0600 hours with three-quarters of an hour artillery preparation.

Chief of Staff of the 6th Army Schmidt estimated that the enemy's actual offensive would not start before January 20.

During the night the replacement of the 376th Infantry Division by the 29th Motorized Division continued; the movements of the artillery were under way when the Russians attacked.

Early that evening a medical commission arrived at the 376th Infantry Division to investigate the effects of hardship on individual soldiers. Investigations would have begun the following day.

In the Orlovka position, which was hard to reach by truck, the last bread rations were issued that day.

Sunday, January 10, 1943

First day of the Russian offensive. Winter sunshine throughout the day.

The Russians attacked punctually at 6 A.M.:

The 21st Army straddling Marinovka (extreme west). The 65th Army between Sovkhoz 1 and Dimitrovka (extended north-west front). The 66th Army attacked in the north, the 64th in the south.

Inside the pocket

2nd Company, Infantry Regiment 71 (west): In view of an Army order that any man who destroyed a Russian tank in close combat would immediately be flown out, a number of soldiers tried to throw bottles of gasoline at the Russian tanks which had been driving around among the bunkers since 6.30 A.M. looking for opportunities for effective action.

3rd Company, Infantry Regiment 71 (south): The company commanders had been summoned to battalion staff headquarters. Telephone lines were destroyed. The company commanders were unable to get back in time for the battle. The company defended itself all day. Company commander Lieutenant H. returned as darkness fell. A Russian tank had been chasing him south of Tsybenko since early afternoon. During the night the company retreated through knee-deep snow.

20th Company, Rumanian Infantry Division (south): On Hill 111.5 an officer from an unknown unit was waiting. Yesterday a battalion from another division had lain here: it had disappeared this morning, he said.

4th Company, Infantry Regiment 71 (south): With the aid of a fleeing corporal of the 2nd Company, Sergeant D. managed to drag the wounded First Lieutenant H. toward the battalion command post. A Russian tank tried to run the group down but in the deep snow did not succeed, in spite of several attempts. The crew of an 88-mm. antiaircraft gun up front waved, meaning the group was to lie down. The gun destroyed the tank by firing at it over the group. When Sergeant D. reached the battalion commander, Captain Müller von Berneck (as sole survivor of the old Reichswehr Company), the latter wept and said: "D., try to get through to the supply column so that at least one of the old gang survives!"

Infantry Regiment 15, Riflemen Battalion (west): Under Captain von Devit, virtually run down by tanks, no longer existent.

3rd Motorized Infantry Division (extreme west): After being penetrated during the day, as well as outflanked, it attempted during the night to withdraw as quickly as possible from the narrow strip at Marinovka.

Motorcycle riflemen of the 29th Infantry Division (west): Bombarded from the side from Cossack Hill; wings badly dented. Retreat attempted during the night.

Heavy Road-building Battalion 540: Enemy advances from Hill 129 toward the village of Dimitrovka. The battalion is destroyed; all very reliable men, none under forty, mostly technical specialists.

Hollow containing headquarters of 29th Motorized Infantry Division (west to northwest): By evening all but one gun destroyed. A survivor of the 44th Infantry Division arrives from the north at midday: farther forward, everything gone. This officer is now ordered to block the northwest entrance to the hollow with fifty men of the 29th Infantry Division.

44th Infantry Division (northwest): Since early morning, clusters of Russian tanks, the roofs packed with infantry; steadily approaching; red flags planted on the tanks; across the steppe, marches and slogans issuing from portable radios and loudspeakers. Behind the tanks, dense columns of infantry. The 44th Division lay on both sides of Cossack Hill, a flat summit. No one dared climb this summit for observation. After the soldiers had recovered from their shock of early morning, they offered resistance. Some of them were very rapidly destroyed.

Corps level in the west: Here the VIII Army Corps and the 14th Panzer Corps were in command. Soon after midday there were great gaps in the front.

113th Infantry Division (north): Promptly at 5.15 A.M. the division underruns the Russian artillery fire, i.e., all important men are well up front; the ensuing Russian attack is cunningly repulsed. It is a minor attack.

60th Motorized Infantry Division and 16th Panzer Division (northern barrier position): Severely damaged.

The 297th Division in the southwest was assigned a tank adviser staff from Army headquarters.

Army Command: To some extent affairs are slipping out of the grasp of the Army Command because they cannot immediately be reproduced on maps and charts.

Monday, January 11, 1943

Second day of the Russian offensive. Bright sunshine. At 11 A.M. radio message from the 3rd Motorcycle Battalion 29: Holding old position.

Focal point is highway toward Novoaleksandrovka in the Rossoshka valley. There are four tanks of the 3rd Motorized Infantry Division here; 170 men, sent in as infantry, of Captain Reinbrecht's combat group from the 29th Motorized Infantry Division, as well as an 88-mm. antiaircraft gun, a light field howitzer, two 75-mm. cannons from tanks, and eight 20-mm. antiaircraft guns. Cable communication functioning to the division, from there to the corps, from there to the Army, thus enabling the latter to give orders. At 10 A.M. a message reaches the focal point: right neighbor, remainder of 44th Infantry Division, retreating rapidly toward the east. Attacking Russians also to be seen on the right.

At noon in front of the headquarters hollow of the 29th Infantry Division an infantry march-past like a parade, red flags in the sunshine. Having approached to within feasible range, this enemy is destroyed.

Early in the afternoon a snow cloud descends from Cossack Hill toward the focal point. It consists of fifty tanks, of English manufacture, every second tank bearing a large red flag. Tank strategy is disregarded. The German soldiers are terrified by the clumsy massiveness of the attack. They try to escape. However, behind them, scattered throughout the hollow, are officers who stop them.

Army level

During the morning minor penetrations are apparent in the north and south, disastrous breakthroughs in the west. Evidently the soldiers from the Karpovka valley, where at least some of them had found warm shelters, are being driven eastward out into the open steppe.

The determined chief of staff of the 6th Army, who could do little, told Captain G., who was flying out: "Raise hell with them if they don't send more planes." After flying out, the captain could say no more to the Luftwaffe colonel in charge than: "Look here, sir, you must send more planes."

Army Group level

Major Toepke, who was desperate, wanted to abandon his contacts at Army Group and Luftwaffe staff level that day and fly back to the pocket. Von Manstein's chief of staff refused him permission. "My dear Toepke, you have seen too much of what's going on here. What do you intend to report to Colonel General Paulus? It is essential that you take really favorable reports to Paulus. At the moment these do not exist."

Army Group headquarters preferred to send seventy officers, who were returning from leave to the 6th Army, completely astray rather than fly them into Stalingrad. Two officers with famous names (von Bismarck and von Below) flew into Stalingrad despite all precautions.

Colonel von B., when reminded that it was the anniversary of Frederick the Great's birthday, said at staff headquarters: "During a troop review in Silesia, Frederick the Great expressed surprise that the honest, harassed soldiers should keep on marching at someone else's orders instead of killing their officers!"

Tuesday, January 12, 1943
Third day of the Russian offensive. Somewhat misty.

Field Marshal Kesselring called on Hitler; discussed sea transport situation in the south. The 5th Panzer Army in Tunis in process of formation. The chotts west of Gabès only passable by established routes. A day of crucial decisions at Wolfsschanze.

In the pocket, remaining troops withdraw from the west side of the pocket to the line Sovkhoz 1, Novoaleksandrovka, and S. The new line appears to be holding. The two commanding generals, Hube in particular, inspected the new terrain and the troops deployed.

In the north, the soldiers of the 16th Panzer Division and the 60th Motorized Infantry Division have been lying for thirty hours facing their positions, which they have been unable to regain. Behind snow walls, units of the 16th Panzer Division have been running about in small circles for thirty hours to keep warm. Then in an artillery bombardment they lost their nerve. A company commander who found himself at the center of the panic turned up at the divisional command post riding a field kitchen at a gallop.

General P. called on Paulus, then went to see von Manstein.

Wednesday, January 13, 1943   Göring's birthday
Fourth day of the Russian offensive.

The landing of a four-motored Junkers 290 was greeted with enthusiasm in the pocket. Seventy-five German and seventy-five Rumanian wounded were stowed in the smooth body of the great plane. At take-off, the allied soldiers slipped on the metal floor into the rear of the plane. Its rear overloaded, the giant aircraft crashed and wiped out the wounded. The day before it had been established that wounded men with lung and brain injuries died at altitudes of more than 3,000 feet. Four planeloads of dead were unloaded at N.

Ahead of the village of Novoaleksandrovka, Slope 1 of the valley bottom (considerably higher slope on the enemy side), remnants of the 29th Motorized Division had been encamped since the previous evening, some sections at the northern entrance to the village. Reconnaissance troops are sent out; a 10-cm. long-bore gun fires on Russian tanks which (visible despite camouflage paint) are maneuvering like insects on the opposite slope. Throughout the day and during the night hours, the soldiers remain where they had been placed the previous evening. Some of them are asleep; fine snow has covered them over. Officers and noncoms keep themselves awake. The Russians hesitate before the new line; all day long they attack in varying degrees of force. Quite early that day, in the south, the Russian Generals Voronov and Rokossovski send in the 57th and 64th Armies from Tsybenko, which has been taken two days earlier.

General Hube of the 14th Panzer Corps, with the remainder of his staff, is at D., already four miles behind Novoaleksandrovka. The advance of the Russians in the south has deprived his defense line of all meaning. Hube distributes his staff officers and the few soldiers still remaining to him close to the edge of the village. In view of the prevailing despair, the general digs himself in and intends to be killed here, for a retreat across the steppe seems just as senseless. The troops have destroyed most of their vehicles and equipment. The men around Hube are counting on a fight to the finish and are ready to face it. In the evening, a few Russian tanks approach.

Captain Behr of the General Staff flew out of the pocket on orders of General Paulus. He carried with him the war journal of the 6th Army as well as letters from Paulus to von Manstein and from Chief of Staff Schmidt to von Manstein's Chief of Staff S. At noon he arrived at Army Group operational headquarters in Taganrog. His instructions were: to present the hopeless situation in the pocket to von Manstein and Hitler; to make it clear to them that the 6th Army would be lost if something really decisive were not done within forty-eight hours.

Why did Paulus send Behr?

Hitler would have regarded General Staff officers as professional pessimists. The attempt to send a general to Hitler had already been made; without success. But perhaps Hitler would not have expected a young, good-looking officer wearing the Knight's Cross.

Moreover, Paulus wished to be sure of having one last eye-witness outside the pocket. Paulus was convinced everyone would be dead within the next few days. Perhaps the pocket would be finished in two days. Behr would not be back by then.

Behr had no high rank to lose, so he would probably not be intimidated by Hitler. Moreover, he was the brother-in-law of one of Hitler's Wehrmacht adjutants. When Behr took off in the morning from Bassargino it was clear the airfield would very soon be gone.

Behr grasped the situation outside, so different from that of the pocket, as soon as he left the airfield building. He wore a mask and remained unaffected by the changed atmosphere. Major Toepke met him and briefed him (also on the fact that he, Toepke, was being, so to speak, held back here). Captain G., another of the minority of pocket officers out here, intercepted Behr as soon as he arrived at Army Group operational headquarters. After that Behr found himself among the outsiders, some of whom, though, he did know from before. General S. greeted him. Von Manstein, surprised, received the new arrival at once. The generals prevented Behr from flying on to Wolfsschanze the same day.

Behr brought along a postcard from Kunowski on which Kunowski referred to signs of disintegration in the pocket. This shook Toepke, because Kunowski, his superior, would not formerly have made such an allusion on an open postcard.

Thursday, January 14, 1943
Fifth day of the Russian offensive.

In the south of the pocket the 297th Infantry Division has been smashed. Rumanian troops deployed there are fleeing in all directions.

Russian tanks and columns are advancing on Novoaleksandrovka and Bassargino, then begin a swing to the east. A Russian
regiment thrusts across Point 502 toward the railway line and
marches eastward along it; mission: to prise out Paulus's staff,
assumed to be in a ravine east of Yablochni.

Sergeant Major Wallrawe wounded in the abdomen. Since the
troops had had no food whatever for some six days, Sergeant
Major Wallrawe survived this injury which, had his stomach been
full, would have killed him.

The motorcycle riflemen west of the village of Novoaleksandrovka spent the whole day without moving from the spot. At
dusk they attacked a Russian staging area from which they would
presumably have been attacked in the dark. They shouted, some
hundred and seventy of them, "Hurrah!" Prompted by these shouts,
about 3,000 soldiers gradually joined in the attack—men who
had found refuge in the village of Novoaleksandrovka.

The attack was particularly successful because the Russians
assumed they were fighting desperate or deranged men.

Once the exhausted men had realized this was a limited attack
and not a breakout from the pocket, they returned to their hiding
places in Novoaleksandrovka and the neighboring hollows.

Starting today, casualty lists are no longer being kept. However,
combat records are to be maintained.

By evening, the Reinbrecht combat group of the 29th Infantry
Division, which had been especially hard pressed by the enemy,
had managed to dig itself in comparatively deeply. During the
night some technicians sent by the division succeeded in getting
two 20-mm. guns functioning again.

Late in the afternoon panic arose on the Bassargino airfield.
Russian tanks were said to be close by. An evacuation of the
airfield was considered. The four fighter planes remaining at the
airfield took off and crashed when trying to land at the Gumrak
airfield inside the pocket. In the evening General Schmidt, chief
of staff of the 6th Army, managed to put an end to the commotion
by telephone.

Morning report of the Army: Only half the troops have been

issued seven ounces of bread. Ammunition so scarce that massed enemy forces facing the front can no longer be fought.

Daily bulletin: Some divisions are fighting with naked blades as they are out of ammunition. Because of enemy superiority (especially in artillery), many cases of freezing to death, and the troops' total exhaustion, no longer possible to hold present positions on west front. Don Army Group's P.S. to this message: Due to continuing inadequate supplies, Army Group no longer counts on Army's position being restored.

Captain Behr's mission

In the morning Captain Behr flew from Taganrog to Wolfsschanze. While in the air he thought up phrases with which to open his address to Hitler; then he forgot the phrases. His brother-in-law met him at the Rastenburg airfield; he informed him of the various moods at headquarters and helped ward off the sentry and officials who wanted to search and question the captain more thoroughly. Behr was able to freshen up in a kind of sleeping-car compartment. Shortly before 11 P.M. he was summoned to the evening briefing with Hitler. Hitler's timetable had not permitted an earlier meeting. Present were: Keitel, Jodl, Schmundt, Bodenschatz, Himmler, Bormann, war-theater specialists, stenographers, Hitler's adjutants, orderlies. Hitler said: "Heil, Captain Behr." This form of address confused Behr; after numerous brief conversations with officers at headquarters, Behr, undernourished, almost collapsing under the burden of his responsibility, might have failed in his mission. Hitler had already turned away to engage in a normal discussion of the situation. Behr interrupted him. The generals held their breath when Hitler was interrupted. Keitel (standing behind Hitler) tried to silence Behr by signaling with his head and eyes. Schmundt showed his annoyance. Behr said: "My Führer, please hear me out, I haven't finished yet." Hitler listened to Behr's recital. He became more and more restless. He had already grasped that something must be done for Stalingrad immediately. He ordered Behr to return the following evening.

Why was Göring not present?

He had his own headquarters train near Wolfsschanze. Under the puritanical limitations of Wolfsschanze or the limited environment of his headquarters train, he was unable to govern. For a long time after the November disaster of Stalingrad he remained here so as not to abandon the field to his enemies. However, in January he emerged from this impossible command center; he intended to devote himself to the employment of the Luftwaffe. But by then he had already fallen into disfavor.

Friday, January 15, 1943
Sixth day of the Russian offensive.

In the morning things were at first strangely quiet. Then the enemy made a surprise penetration on the north slope of the hill, west of N.

The R. valley was to be held until 6 P.M. The 76th Infantry Division tried to hold it; the victorious 113th Infantry Division in the north tried to reach safety. The combat group that had been defending Novoaleksandrovka for several days abandoned this village at 11 A.M. The evasive movement continued southward, the Russians having destroyed the south side of the pocket.

Near B. threats are required to keep the soldiers in their holes; at those points where they are still maintaining defenses in the R. valley, some of the soldiers are so apathetic that they sit in their holes and fire into the air. At 1 P.M. the soldiers deployed east of Novoaleksandrovka are permitted to retreat. This is the Reinbrecht combat group. As soon as the men leave their holes they are shot at from all sides. They are unable to hide in the snow. The Russians follow them with openly deployed artillery and heavy machine guns.

Captain Reinbrecht:

Early in the morning still warm; blood pulsing properly through his body. Ten officers drive the soldiers to their positions. At

1 P.M. Reinbrecht wonders whether it would be better to wait in the holes until evening, i.e., to let the Russians pass them by, or to allow the men to escape toward the rear across a bare hill. After his first few leaps to the rear, he is severely wounded. A few minutes ago he was wondering whether this was the right course; had he decided otherwise he would still be sitting intact in his cover. Hope deserts him. His body gets colder. While being transported to central Stalingrad, the severely wounded man suffers from frostbite. For several days he lies unattended; then he dies.

While the retreat of a unit from the R. valley is being prepared toward evening, some sections having already started out, the Russians attack. A middle-aged officer decided quite calmly to lead the departing soldiers forward again to their previous position at the edge of S. "Back!" he shouted. Thereupon the soldiers fled back, tried to get out of the R. valley. The Russians turned up in the midst of this confusion. They followed hesitatingly.

During the night Russian forces thrust forward in long wedges toward the railway circling Stalingrad. Automobiles containing staff equipment are discovered in various farms. Illustrated magazines are stacked up in piles, but also lie scattered on the village street of S.

Von Seydlitz: "I simply can't see any ultimate meaning in the wretched extinction and hunting down of German soldiers by openly deployed Russian tanks." Schmidt: "Tell everyone you think should listen that the Army has been betrayed and deserted at the highest level."

During the nights between January 8 and 11, the 376th Infantry Division has been replaced in the western tip and since then has constantly changed position; tonight it is overtaken by Russian tank spearheads and flees.

Wherever roads approach from the west, tough officers man a theoretical line to intercept escaping soldiers as well as those retreating in orderly fashion.

Daily Army bulletin

Despite heroic fighting by the 16th Panzer Division, hill two miles southeast of Point 139.7, surrounded on three sides for several days, has been lost after fierce attacks. . . . Impossible to reoccupy hill due to shortage of ammunition and forces.

Hitler received Captain Behr at the evening briefing as promised. "Give my regards to Paulus," he said. "I'm doing all I can." Friends gave Behr a sack of bacon to distribute among friends in the pocket. While Behr was still present, Hitler gave Field Marshal Milch the promised special powers. Following the evening briefing, Hitler said to Field Marshal Milch, Secretary of State in the Reich Air Ministry, an enterprising man: "Since the decision has been made to hold Stalingrad, all resources must be employed toward that end. It is my impression that everyone there is doing his best and that, all in all, everything has been done that could be done: nevertheless, I demand that in future 300 tons be flown into the fortress daily so that it can hold out and strong Russian forces can be kept tied up. I herewith empower you with the necessary special authority to give orders and instructions to all command posts of the various sections of the armed forces."

Saturday, January 16, 1943
Seventh day of the Russian offensive. Driving snow, temperature 30° Centigrade below zero.

The Bassargino airfield was evacuated that day; Army operational headquarters transferred to a point farther inside the pocket.

Since morning, combat groups of the 29th Infantry Division, remnants of the 44th Infantry Division, remnants of the 76th Infantry Division, scattered remains of the 3rd Motorized Infantry Division, now without motors, sections of the 376th and 384th Divisions, had been moving toward the circular railway around

Stalingrad. The Russians advanced cautiously toward the east and overtook the fleeing troops. They were cautious because they suspected traps.

First major offensive procedure

The operative pincer movements planned by Russian headquarters were not attempted. Instead, the Russian armies pressed like a flood from west to east. From time to time they assembled to observe how the encircled troops deployed themselves ahead of them. On January 17 there was a meeting of commanders. Prevailing opinion was in favor of waiting, of reassembling. The Russian Generals Rokossovski and Voronov, however, insisted on immediate resumption of operations. This was the first time the Russians tried a major offensive on a pocket. An impression arose of hesitancy, of a certain indecision, of pauses between the various thrusts. Official reports to Voronov's and Rokossovski's headquarters were made in such a way that the maps at headquarters showed a series of logical pincer movements, as desired by headquarters. Pauses or hesitation did not appear as such: they were the result of advancing Russian troops and tanks having continually to reorganize.

Daily bulletin of the 6th Army

Enemy continues mass assaults against south, southwest, and west fronts; however, repulsed in heavy fighting at new defense line. Supply situation disastrous. Owing to fuel shortage, troops no longer able to move rations to the front. Many companies on the west front without rations for two days. Troops exposed unprotected all day, temperature 22 degrees below zero, without bunkers, to attacks by Russian Stuka squadrons with superheavy bombs. Our own Stukas, fighter, and reconnaissance planes out of action or flown elsewhere.

Army Staff Colonel S., who was on an inspection trip, discussed with General Strecker, commanding the northern part of the pocket, the question of what was to happen in the end. At this time talks were held with many hundreds of staff officers on the alternatives of breakout or death. Army Command allowed individual freedom of choice of any action except desertion.

Sunday, January 17, 1943
Eighth day of the Russian offensive.

Army Command was again able to draw a theoretical front line from north to south on their maps and more or less to occupy it.

Lieutenant Colonel Langkeit assembled all survivors of the pocket Panzer regiments in the Stalingradski ravine, not far from Army operational headquarters, so that the end might be awaited there jointly. Room was found for everyone in bunkers or holes in the ground.

During the night no aircraft have landed on the improvised substitute pocket airfield at Gumrak. An investigation is ordered. Five aircraft did land. Since no ground crews were there, the tonnage had to be handed out to passing troops, who appeared to be in a state of disintegration.

Colonel General Paulus sent a radio message to the Führer stating that the Luftwaffe was betraying the pocket; further radio messages at noon. Telephone calls from von Manstein to Milch; Göring phones Milch; Milch phones Generals Fiebig and von Richthofen; airfields and crews are canvassed; a further accusation by radio from the Army in the pocket. The point is argued between the Luftwaffe Command and the 6th Army whether planes can land in Gumrak in view of the artillery bombardment of the airfield; one aircraft that landed had all its fuel siphoned off by passing troops so that it could not return. Among those outside the pocket who are in telephone communication, it is arranged that emissaries from the Luftwaffe should be flown into the pocket the following day to investigate the point under dispute.

The Charkov Army radio station broadcasts a special program for Stalingrad. Program sequence:

> Old St. Stephen's still stands—all is well;
> Never mind what may change round about. . . .
> Love for Vienna is in my blood. . . .
> St. Stephen's stands proud in the crowded streets.
> The heart of Vienna for centuries beats. . . .
> We Viennese, we Viennese, we may seek fortune at our ease. . . .
> Say, is our Danube still ever so blue? . . .
> Little bird from Vienna, fly back to my home. . . .

Daily Army bulletin

Starting at midnight, waves of enemy attacks on the fortress, now without fighter cover and with almost no antiaircraft protection. If the promised increase in air supplies does not commence immediately, there is no prospect whatever of holding out.

On the northeast, west, and northwest fronts the 6th Army has on the whole held its positions against further heavy attacks. Numerous local crises occasioned by ammunition and fuel shortage. . . . Because of inadequate supplies the fortress is expecting the worst. Many soldiers have starved to death.

Monday, January 18, 1943
Ninth day of the Russian offensive.

Fighter planes and bombers are on their way from France to relieve the pocket defenders. Milch is planning to use gliders. He has recovered from his automobile accident of the previous day and calls on von Manstein; the two field marshals see eye to eye.

Inside the pocket, the arrival of a few planes dropping supplies by parachute is at least an indication of air support. After dark a dozen aircraft land at Gumrak. A study of air supplies yields the following figures:

		Tons
January	4	250
January	5	150
January	6	45
January	7	115
January	8	99
January	9	196.5
January	13	119.1
January	14	120
January	15	92
January	16	72
January	17	nothing
January	18	27
January	19	60
January	20	55.4
January	21	97.3

Daily Army bulletin

Fuel situation resulting from failure of air supply is crippling all movement, including the supplying of troops with rations. Continuous air attacks. Gumrak airfield open for landing.

Radio message from the 6th Army:

My Führer, your orders re supplying the Army are not being carried out. Gumrak airfield open for landing since January 15, all clear for night landings, ground crew available. Request immediate measures, situation extremely critical.

Radio message:

Luftwaffe's objections interpreted as excuses. Luftwaffe units, i.e., airborne personnel, have established that landing is possible from every direction. Runway considerably enlarged, ground organization including all equipment in perfect working order, as previously at Bassargino. Commander in Chief has made direct request to Führer to take immediate steps, constant delays by Luftwaffe having already cost many lives.

Radio message during the night: "Still no aircraft arriving. Army requests aircraft crews be ordered to land."

Tuesday, January 19, 1943
Tenth day of the Russian offensive.

Daily Army bulletin

Enemy resumed mass attacks on the west front against left wing of 76th and right wing of 44th Infantry Divisions, but was repulsed. Some airdrops not found because of snowdrifts; collecting same much hampered by fuel shortage.

At 11 A.M. a Luftwaffe officer, Major Thiel, landed in the pocket. By 4 P.M. his plane had not yet been unloaded. Large number of enemy fighters over the fortress, although not flying below 3,000 feet. Whenever anything moves on the ground at the airfield, three waiting Russian battle planes drop bombs. If they miss their target, Russian artillery takes over. At this airfield the apathetic soldiers scarcely bother to carry out orders.

Officer of the Luftwaffe Thiel was taken to Paulus and his Chief of Staff Schmidt. The principal Army staff officers were present. Paulus said at noon: "The Luftwaffe has not trusted my staff's information and so has betrayed the whole operation." At two thirty he said: "You are talking here to dead men. The Luftwaffe has deserted us. Airdrops alone mean death to the Army!" Outside the pocket Milch gave instructions to accept in silence the 6th Army's accusations directed at the Luftwaffe, conditions in the pocket being so difficult. Field Marshal von Manstein pursued a similar temporizing policy.

Panzer Lieutenant Colonel Langkeit, flown out of the pocket during the morning, was immediately put to work at the K. airfield in the organization of air supplies. Von Manstein was aiming at a kind of self-administration in the air-supply system outside the pocket by the 6th Army; he felt that officers from the pocket were best able to bridge the gulf between the pocket and the areas outside.

Colonel Adam, one of Paulus's adjutants, said that day to an officer in the pocket, a friend of his: "I tell you, there are 150,000 of us left, but those 150,000 are all ready to commit treason." The Communist writer Weinert read poetry to newly-captured prisoners of war. Captured officers were singled out and taken to a classroom in the village school at K. on the Don where the writer Weinert was waiting for them. The prisoners, most of them intractable, offered less resistance to poetry, even if it contained propaganda.

Wednesday, January 20, 1943
Eleventh day of the Russian offensive.

East of P. and Bassargino, General Staff officers attempted to trace a front. The staffs of the 14th Panzer Corps, the 3rd Motorized Infantry Division, and the 29th Infantry Division assembled in the Tigoda ravine.

Army's morning bulletin: Withdrawal of right wing of 60th Motorized Infantry Division carried out according to plan; heavy weapons left behind (fuel shortage).

Daily bulletin: Withdrawal of northwest front begun. Due to fuel shortage, many men, weapons, and much equipment will be lost.

Paulus sent the following radio message to Zeitzler:

Fortress can only be held for a few more days. Lack of supplies has weakened men and immobilized weapons. Last airfield will shortly be lost, supplies will thus sink to a minimum. Basis for battle orders to hold Stalingrad has ceased to exist. Russians can already break through along various fronts, since whole sections are missing due to men dying. Heroism of commanding officers and soldiers nevertheless unimpaired. To utilize this for final blow, I intend shortly before the collapse to issue orders for all troop units to undertake an organized breakout to the southwest. Some groups will get through and cause confusion behind Russian front, while if we remain here everyone is certain to be killed, since prisoners will also die of hunger and cold. Propose flying out a few specialists, officers and men, for use in further combat. Orders for this must be issued without delay, as presumably there is not much time left for flying in. Please designate officers by name, myself obviously excluded.

(signed): Paulus

The following reply was dispatched:

Radio message received. Coincides fully with my proposal of four days ago. Proposal repeated to Führer. Führer has decided:
1. Re breakout: Führer to make final decision. When time comes, kindly send me further radio message.
2. Re flying out: Führer has for the time being refused permission. Please send Zitzewitz for further presentation of proposal. I will take him personally to the Führer.

(signed): Zeitzler

Two officers found an air-dropped food package in a cellar; they ate the contents and then shot themselves separately.

Thursday, January 21, 1943
Twelfth day of the Russian offensive.

Generals Pfeffer and von Seydlitz requested Paulus that day to terminate fighting. Paulus, who had seen for himself the sufferings of his troops during the preceding days (while his staff was being transferred), consulted his chief of staff (Schmidt), his Ia (Elchlepp), and his IIa (Adam). Of these officers, Ia was in favor of holding out; he was still counting on Operation "Lion" for the final phase: a breakout in individual groups in all directions. Paulus did not know what to do. There was no interpreter among the Army staff officers. Captain von N. of the IV Army Corps was summoned by radio. During the discussion Paulus sat next to von N. Paulus said: "What we are now doing is quite possibly treason." A little later he said: "What am I to do if the Führer does not agree?" In the depressed atmosphere of that day they wanted to act on the Russian offer of capitulation of January 9. The following letter was translated into Russian by Von N.:

To Colonel General of the Artillery Voronov:
I am prepared to enter into negotiations with you on the basis of your terms of January 9. I request that you order an armistice from January 23 starting at . . . hours. My authorized representatives will

arrive in two automobiles with a white flag at . . . on January 23 on the road parallel to the line from G. to the Konnaia-Kotluban siding.

Commander in Chief of the 6th Army

6th Army's morning bulletin: Since January 16 only thirty-six shells for light field howitzers have arrived, several thousand fired; for each barrel, thirty shells still available. Supplies of fuel and rations correspondingly low.

Daily bulletin: In unimaginably heroic and desperate fighting, the divisions on the west front attempted to ward off massed enemy attacks with artillery and tanks in a fluctuating battle. Numerous deep breakthroughs barely intercepted; counterthrusts undertaken by handfuls of men temporarily halted enemy regiments; a number of tanks destroyed, some in close combat. Since nightfall, 60th Motorized Infantry Division, 113th and 76th Infantry Divisions, fighting their way back (enemy in their rear) on Nadesha line— three miles east of Gontchara—which is to be held until January 22. . . . 44th Infantry Division apparently annihilated.

Nature, sunshine. Crows have set to work on the eyes of a frozen corpse on a slope. Birds are uncommon in the steppe. The small white sun, visible through a pale haze, has discarded its usual whitewash, but this doesn't help. A day of open sky brings merciless cold, air masses from Astrakhan that have no intention of adjusting to human standards.

Friday, January 22, 1943
Thirteenth day of the Russian offensive.

The Chief of General Staff of the 6th Army Schmidt proposed to his commander in chief that, in view of the situation, "dying be properly organized." What he meant was the handing over of field hospitals to the enemy. Paulus did not want to decide this without consulting his superiors. Paulus and his chief of staff disagreed before witnesses.

Army's morning bulletin: In fierce day-long fighting on the

185

north, west, and southwest fronts, enemy succeeded in deeply penetrating the southwest front. Almost all ammunition already fired, some signs of disintegration. With the last weapons, twenty enemy tanks destroyed. West front defended only by scattered strongpoints; 76th, 297th, 29th Motorized, and 3rd Motorized Infantry Divisions wiped out.

The Russian front-line radio station, established to influence the pocket, broadcast:

> Every rose speaks of love,
> Every rose says, I love.

Staff Paymaster H. in the eastern part of the pocket made suggestions for a Stalingrad crest that were forwarded to higher authorities. Colonel Adam had to spend all day in the area around Stalingrad trying to locate a spot for an emergency landing field; he returned to headquarters that evening wet through. At times he had sunk up to his chest in snow hollows. Among the 305th and 79th Infantry Divisions in the east of the pocket the rumor obstinately persisted that the Führer had flown into the pocket; also that some paratroop regiments were being flown in.

The 389th Infantry Division in the northwest tip near S. on the Volga discussed a suggestion made by the LI Corps of a sudden breakout eastward across the Volga, with perhaps three neighboring divisions, against Paulus's orders. The idea was to move first toward the east, then back across the Volga west and south, finally reaching the German lines. The inhabitants of the Kirgiz steppe might not be hostile. The plan was then dropped. Lieutenant Colonel F., of Corps General Heitz's staff, ordered a staff driver to take him to the airfield. There he forced his way through to an airplane under pretext of having been ordered to take charge of important organizational measures outside the pocket. The lieutenant colonel's desertion was discovered after the staff driver's return to corps headquarters. F., who reported to Army Group headquarters with his alleged instructions, was shot the following day outside the pocket on grounds of cowardice. F.'s general, known as Daddy Heitz, found it incredible that a fellow officer should desert him like that after so many years with his staff.

Saturday, January 23, 1943
Fourteenth day of the Russian offensive.

In the afternoon Army staff headquarters transferred to the command post of the 71st Infantry Division, then to south Stalingrad.

Divisional staffs are now of the opinion that during the retreat the wounded will be better off remaining behind where they are. This view is opposed by a certain amount of emotion, but on the other hand it seems more practical, and from a medical standpoint more sound, to leave the wounded well cared for in the hands of the enemy than to give them a few more days' freedom in Stalingrad without proper care.

That evening the last airplane leaves an improvised air strip near Stalingrad.

Sections of the 29th, 3rd, and 376th Infantry Divisions, etc., retreating on the highway from Gumrak to Stalingrad, were subject to night attacks by Russian planes on the crowded road. The columns of vehicles could not leave the road, so they kept on going straight ahead while the planes bombarded them for about four hours.

Of Supply Regiment 389 the following survived the night:

Second Lieutenant (Eng.)	M.
Sergeant Major	Köstler
Sergeant	Bernhard
Sergeant	Lorenz
Staff Private First Class	W.
Corporals	Witte, Mai, Verheyen
Privates First Class	Pfeifer, Peikert, and Rühmenapp

For days units of the 1st Rumanian Cavalry Division and the 20th Rumanian Infantry Division had been encamped along the road to Gumrak, occupying all quarters; from time to time military police seized Rumanian marauders.

Subordinate Rumanian units had joined up with some of the units streaming toward Stalingrad; it was impossible to get rid of this influx, which represented a further demand on rations; these comrades clung stubbornly to the German troops, believing them to be the most likely source of food.

Sunday, January 24, 1943
Fifteenth day of the Russian offensive. Sunshine.

Thousands of soldiers are wandering about the streets of Stalingrad. The Russians are not firing much. At various street corners in the city, food is being cooked in saucepans and frying pans. Crowds of soldiers are approaching the city from Gumrak. During the night the Tigoda ravine was abandoned; retreat to a theoretical line in the snow, partially marked by pegs and string. This was now said to be the final defense line.

Toward noon the west front was officially withdrawn to the outskirts of Stalingrad.

Because of his knowledge of Russian, Captain von N. was summoned to Army headquarters for the second time and given a royal reception. He was offered cigarettes, coffee, French cognac. The captain was to be available to the Army Command as an interpreter. It was desirable, said Schmidt, that the person of the commander in chief and the officers immediately around him should not become involved in close combat. Von Elchlepp and the Ic were to know nothing of this plan. The main idea was: the commander in chief has not surrendered, he has been taken prisoner.

Several times during the day Paulus spoke of having to shoot himself. General Schmidt, on the other hand, would take no part in discussions; he clung to his own line of thought: smooth dissolving of the pocket, then smooth transition to prisoner-of-war status.

Around noon the chief of staff of the LI Corps summoned all available subordinate officers to a meeting near a ruined factory. When the chief of staff told them: "You're on your own now; the battle has been lost, I wish you luck" (and shook hands with them), the men who until that moment had been led could not immediately make use of their freedom of choice, since their ration supply continued to depend on their being part of the organization. So for the time being freedom meant merely that they were obliged to change their conditions of subordination. Captain Z. placed himself under the garrison command of central Stalingrad.

A bevy of officers under F. set themselves up in the block of houses in Map Square Qu 16 (theater), the cellar of which held 400 wounded. There was a prospect of obtaining rations here.

Captain G.:
He had found some bread wrapped in insulating paper, probably part of an airdrop. He was with a group of soldiers still outside Stalingrad; the balka, a side ravine of the Tigoda ravine, lay parallel to the direction in which the Russians were attacking. Some Army telephone connections installed here were still intact; until recently there had been three staffs here. G. picked up the telephones and listened; then he ate the bread. On the one hand satisfaction, on the other fear of getting a bullet in his stomach. G. got the bullet in his stomach an hour later when he tried to creep out of the ravine.

Paulus dispatched the following radio message to Hitler:

. . . Signs of disintegration on the south, north, and west fronts. Unified command no longer possible. East front only slightly changed. Eighteen thousand wounded without dressings or medication of any kind. 44th, 76th, 100th, 305th, and 384th Infantry Divisions wiped out. Many gaps in the front due to deep penetrations. Strongpoints

and possibilities of cover now available only in the city itself, further
defense meaningless. Collapse inevitable. To save those still surviving,
Army requests consent to immediate capitulation.

(signed): Paulus

Needless to say, Hitler refused to consider a capitulation.

Supreme Command of the Army asked for nominations for
possible citations and promotions inside the pocket.

Exhausted General Leyser

About four miles from Stalingrad, remnants of the 29th Motorized Infantry Division, now without vehicles, managed to disengage themselves from the pursuing Russians. For the past
fifteen days General Leyser had hardly slept. He was marching
along the bottom of a ravine as deep as an eight-story building.
His face covered with sweat as he fell into a snow hole, snow up
to his hips; he just managed to hold onto his carbine. After a
desperate march, the sound of engines coming from vehicles on
the Gumrak–Stalingrad road. The general, three officers, soldiers,
and ten noncoms sought the road. On reaching it, the general
collapsed. An officer gave orders to halt some of the passing
vehicles. The drivers placed the general in the cab of a truck.
This was the first time they had ever given shelter to a general;
they offered him food. On the outskirts of Stalingrad the general
set up his command post. A battery there still had its guns facing
east in the traditional manner. Here there were still optimism,
electric light, cognac offered. The general fell asleep at once.

6th Army's morning bulletin: In the city proper, frightful conditions. Some 20,000 uncared-for wounded looking for shelter
in ruined buildings; a similar number of starving, frostbitten,
roaming soldiers, most of them without weapons.

Daily bulletin: During the fighting for Stalingrad, units of the
1st Rumanian Cavalry and 20th Infantry Divisions had stood
shoulder to shoulder with their German comrades and fought
magnificently to the end: their deeds merited praise in the chronicle
of this unique struggle.

Monday, January 25, 1943
Sixteenth day of the Russian offensive.

The 297th Infantry Division, led by Moritz von Drebbe, marched to the Russian lines; no soldiers from the neighboring divisions joined them, but no one fired either. The former president of the Supreme Military Court, General Heitz of the VIII Corps, ordered his troops to fire on the capitulating neighboring staff of von Seydlitz. Some officers were killed. On the other hand, since January 20 some 120,000 of the remaining 150,000 soldiers had ceased to fight.

Roughly 150,000 soldiers were still hiding in the thirteen miles of ruins that had once been Stalingrad.

6th Army's morning bulletin: The swastika flag hoisted on the tallest building of the central part of the city, so that the final battle could be fought under this emblem.

Daily bulletin
Fierce attacks by superior artillery and tanks, and weaker, hesitant infantry attacks under way. Western perimeter of Stalingrad being held, generally speaking; suburb of Minina lost. 11th Artillery Corps fighting with only a few heavy weapons, very little ammunition, and no food. . . . Waves of violent enemy air attacks over the whole city. Number of wounded, starving, roaming soldiers growing hourly.

Tuesday, January 26, 1943:
Seventeenth day of the Russian offensive.   Driving snow
during the night, and strong wind.

The Russian Generals Voronov and Rokossovski split the pocket in two.

The meeting of the Russian 21st Army with the 13th Sharpshooters Division approaching from the east took place at the cost of the 100th German Rifleman Division. Music, presentation of a flag, speeches, the Russian Generals M., T., K., Voronov, and Rokossovski meet at this point for a visit to the front.

The assembled remnants of the staff of the IV Army Corps and the 71st Infantry Division (the "Lucky"), under Generals Pfeffer and Alexander von Hartmann, waited with Colonels Crome and Wulz in a bunker for the end to come. When the Russians attacked, they climbed with Alexander von Hartmann onto a railway embankment and, standing upright, fired on the Russians until the latter shot and killed General von Hartmann. The result was an immediate dampening of enthusiasm. The officers left the embankment. Late that afternoon M. formed a unit of 280 men to break out toward the southwest, and the attempt was made that evening. The same day General Stempel of the destroyed 371st Infantry Division shot himself at Pfeffer's command post.

Major General W. said to officer B. in surprise: "Why don't you salute me?"

The last remaining company of an artillery regiment is killed off with grenade throwers.

When Lieutenant Colonel von Zitzewitz of the General Staff reported to Hitler on the pocket remnant, Hitler said in a subdued voice, considered by many of his colleagues to be fatherly: "Human beings recover quickly!"

Colonel W. recovers

In Poland Colonel W. was still a captain. He saw seven of his officer friends killed. This sacrifice he regarded as a concession to victory. In France he lost two more friends; thereafter he was cautious about making new friends. However, he could not overlook the fact that he always felt attracted to the young men trained by him. In Serbia he lost some of his younger soldiers, who were ambushed. In Greece—he only got as far as Salonica—two of his men were killed by fire from his own side. In southern Russia there was a shortage of artillery. The soldiers, mud clinging to their feet, were ambushed. While crossing the Dniester a bunker had been overlooked; that cost the lives of fifteen soldiers trained by W. During the winter, along the Mius, W. lost a further forty men in dead and wounded, among them his friend Lieutenant M. In the spring of 1942 W. had only twelve men of his original personnel. By November he had lost eight in front of Stalingrad. Relief arrived in October to enable W. to enter Rynok. The insufficiently trained relief troops fell as they arrived. Thirty days before the formation of the pocket W. decided to save at least one of the four regulars remaining to him. On January 10, at 6 A.M., after three-quarters of an hour artillery preparation, the large-scale offensive against the pocket began. W.'s unit survived the barrage without losses. Some of his men tried to attack the Russian tanks with bottles of gasoline. That day three of the remaining four regulars died. For two hours a tank pursued Sergeant D. across a snow field. D. arrived exhausted at Colonel W.'s command post, which was protected by one remaining gun. W. had the wounded D. taken to the airfield. W. got out of Stalingrad in time, wounded. He recovered in France, formed a new company. The company was lost in Jassy, Rumania. Since W. had been wounded again by this time, he had a chance to recover from this shock. He took part in a battle in the Pusta at the end of 1944. He was now in command of a Panzer unit, hoping not to lose all his soldiers this time. When he was shot out of four successive tanks one day in December, he sat down in a furrow of a field and wept (light infantry fire enveloped him). W. recovered after four weeks in the country in time to participate in the defense of Lake Achen in Bavaria.

Wednesday, January 27, 1943
Eighteenth day of the Russian offensive.

At Army Group headquarters in Taganrog, staff officers were waiting for the fighting in Stalingrad to come to an end. Each officer from the pocket who happened to be at Army Group headquarters that day was assigned another officer whose job it was to protect him from thoughtless actions or remarks.

In some sections of the east front of the pocket, regular duties were still being carried out. Screening of reserves was attempted. During the afternoon Colonel General Paulus arrived at the 14th Panzer Corps command post, spoke with General Schlömer, deputy commander of the 14th Panzer Corps; despite all the suffering that weighed upon him, Paulus came to no decision.

Colonel M., chief of staff of the 14th Panzer Corps, called on Chief of General Staff of the Army Schmidt regarding termination of the fighting. Schmidt replied: "We know the position —orders are: fighting is to continue." M. asked what the soldiers without ammunition were to do? Schmidt: "They have knives or they must bite." Thereupon the first administrative officer of the 14th Panzer Corps staff committed suicide. On hearing this, his Commander in Chief M. rushed out of the command post and disappeared in the partially destroyed industrial area.

That evening the commander of the 29th Infantry Division, General Leyser, decided to terminate the fighting on the 28th. The deputy commanding general of the 14th Panzer Corps turned up, Leyser's superior. On the way he had been wounded in the shin by a ricochet. The senior general put himself under Leyser's command; Leyser assigned General Schlömer a place in the command post, where he immediately fell into a deathlike sleep.

Thursday, January 28, 1943
Nineteenth day of the Russian offensive.

General von Daniels took over the forsaken command of the 14th Panzer Corps. He summoned the divisional commanders and advised them to surrender the following day. Paulus was informed of this seizure of power by von Daniels. He dismissed von Daniels. He succeeded in persuading the divisional commanders by telephone not to capitulate the next morning. General von Daniels then capitulated at least with the 376th Infantry Division.

The main topic of the situation report to Hitler in Wolfsschanze was the re-formation of the 6th Army. Hitler placed great hopes in the S.S. Panzer divisions newly arrived in southern Russia. Hitler cautious. Hitler puts forward the idea of whether it might not be possible to evacuate the Demiansk pocket. He considers the capture of Leningrad more important than the maintenance of this pocket.

Friday, January 29, 1943
Twentieth day of the Russian offensive.

German soldiers, wounded, and Russians stand about together in some confusion in the Stalingrad terrain. Only a few officers and old noncoms receive permission to fire individually on Russian infantry, in order to avoid endangering their own bewildered compatriots.

Summoned by Paulus, General Schlömer, deputy commander of the 14th Panzer Corps who had taken refuge with General Leyser the previous day, resumes his post. He capitulates toward evening.

Saturday, January 30, 1943
Twenty-first day of the Russian offensive.

Colonel General Paulus considers the idea of blowing himself up.

At noon, under a brilliant blue sky, the Russians held a low-altitude flyby of several squadrons.

Hitler promoted Paulus to the rank of field marshal. Decorations for the men and officers were distributed.

During the night, attack of the 3rd Battalion 577 in the north pocket to capture Warehouse 6d with three assault groups.

With sections of the 295th Infantry Division, General Korfes recaptured part of a barracks building.

German assault troop activity in . . . Street met with some success. Russian artillery bombarded central Stalingrad. The concrete vault of the department store under which the Army staff was ensconced held firm. General Roske, commander of central Stalingrad, refused to hoist a German flag on his command post at noon. The soldiers who had already tied the flag to ropes were given counterorders. The flag would have served the Russian artillery as a point of reference. Most of the telephone lines had been disrupted. Three companies of fortress soldiers were formed from soldiers roaming Red Square in Stalingrad. After two hours they had dispersed again. That day some seventeen reliable soldiers were protecting the field marshal.

In the evening, near the New Theater, Major P. banged his head against a high pile. It consisted of bodies, frozen stiff. From a hygienic point of view, this was fortunate; had the Stalingrad disaster taken place at a warmer time of year there would have been widespread epidemics. In the third hour of morning, General Roske, commander of central Stalingrad, decided to receive an enemy truce officer. The Russians sent a captain. This truce officer was sent back, the German command being entitled to at least a staff officer. Thereupon the Russians sent a major from General Staff. When this truce officer, accompanied by an interpreter, entered the cellar, General Schmidt, chief of the Army staff, also came into the room. He said: "What are these chimpanzees doing here?" Officers of Roske's staff requested the senior officer to be more careful. Negotiations then took place as to whether the officers of the 6th Army were to be permitted to retain their so-called cold weapons (side knives, daggers, swords) after what amounted to unconditional surrender. The condition was rejected by the opposite side.

During the night of January 30/31, the thought occurred to the Russian General Voronov that at this juncture Paulus might make use of the ice on the Volga as a landing strip to fly out of the pocket. He gave orders by telephone that the artillery on the east bank was to keep a strict watch. His subordinates assured him that the ice did not form a smooth surface; moreover, the ice was mined; Russian artillery on the east bank of the Volga kept a strict lookout for planes taking off.

Sunday, January 31, 1943

German reconnaissance planes against a brilliant blue winter sky. General Strecker's north pocket relatively quiet.

In the southern section of Stalingrad, a gray, dismal morning; not a single shot was fired. Major Z. was standing in the early-morning light in front of the main entrance to the department store. Russian soldiers almost stumbled on the mine barricade in front of the main entrance; this would have entailed complications. Major Z. warned them. In the corridors of the department store's cellar, many Russians and Germans. In the special cellar provided for the Army Communications Regiment, transmitting and receiving equipment was being destroyed. Some people said: "The field marshal is going to shoot himself," so Major Z. was sent out by members of the Army staff to look for Paulus and prevent this. Everyone was haggard from lack of sleep, overtired. Soldiers in the cellar passageways had seen a general. In various cellar rooms, papers were being burned. Z. saw the field marshal in the court-yard of the department store; Paulus was observing events; he did not appear to be armed. Z. followed the field marshal for nearly an hour at some distance. The soldiers scarcely knew the field marshal, but they knew his name. Some soldiers saluted respect-fully because the officer was a general. Late that morning the field marshal, some generals, and the senior staff officers of the Army were taken away by automobiles as prisoners of war. At the command post of the garrison commander of central Stalin-grad, the newly promoted General Roske, who had surrendered central Stalingrad together with the Army staff, a frugal lunch was prepared for the Russian officers who were now arriving in larger numbers. All the German officers were tense. The fact that some of the senior commanders in Stalingrad were tense to the point of physical exhaustion was partly because they were unable to account for the whereabouts of 35,000 Russian prisoners. The generals did not know whether these Russians had been receiving any rations toward the end. At one time, some of the prisoners were being transported from points in the east of the pocket to the west. They could not be accounted for during the final phase.

At noon the People's Commissar for the Munitions Industry Ageyev arrived at the Russian Don front staff headquarters; he requested 300 captured vehicles and permission to attend the interrogation of Field Marshal Paulus. The German generals, including Paulus, had been taken to S., where they were allowed to have a meal. In the afternoon Paulus was taken to General Voronov's staff blockhouse: there was a room there secured with a double door. Neither Comrade Voronov nor Comrade Rokossovski had any practical experience in interrogating a German field marshal. The photographer Karmen was allowed to be present and take pictures; the munitions commissar was permitted to sit in an adjoining room and listen in. In the anteroom of the blockhouse, Paulus asked how he might distinguish Voronov from Rokossovski (the two generals, who were waiting, heard this, as did the interpreter); Paulus appeared before Voronov and Rokossovski and raised his hand in the Hitler salute. He was asked to sit down. He did not accept a cigarette.

Voronov said: "We suggest that you immediately issue orders to the German troops who are continuing to offer resistance in the northwestern part of Stalingrad to avoid useless bloodshed." Paulus would not give such orders. Rokossovski now took a cigarette, whereupon Paulus also accepted one. Voronov suggested that Paulus consider the situation and issue orders to the remaining German troops to surrender. Paulus, whose nerves were on edge, refused. Voronov then asked him what diet would be suitable for his state of health. The question surprised Paulus; he asked for help not for himself but for the sick officers and men of his army. Voronov had already gone into Paulus's health with Dr. Renoldi, chief medical officer of the 6th Army. The discussion dragged on into the evening. Paulus was worn out. Finally Voronov said: "We wish to point out to the field marshal that because of his attitude many of the troops under his command will be destroyed tomorrow." Paulus then stood up, raised his right arm. Ageyev, the munitions commissar, who had heard it all, congratulated Voronov and Rokossovski on the restrained, effective manner in which they had conducted the interrogation.

Transfer of 100,000 men to a new state of organization

The new organization, that of captivity, absorbed the prisoners-of-war of the 6th Army (equaling in number the inhabitants of a large city) reluctantly. It was more than the Russians could handle; it was mostly the rear echelons of the Russian armies that were now in Stalingrad, the combat troops being already en route for other theaters; the staffs that had been in command here were being dispersed. On February 1 the camp at the . . . factory received millet porridge, fish, and twenty ounces of wet bread per head. A tank drove mistakenly into a column of prisoners. That evening the kitchen burned down at Camp Beketovka. For nine days there was no hot food. Officers were first quartered in somewhat more spacious officers' barracks. In the environs of Stalingrad, columns of prisoners were led through the snow; often they marched without guards. The final marching column stretched from . . . to . . . ; between January and June, 1943, most of those organized in this way died. At Camp V. the prisoners smashed the latrines and burned the wood for fuel; in March the incubation period of the typhus bacilli contained in the lice the soldiers had been carrying around on their bodies since late fall was up; in Camp Beketovka alone, . . . prisoners died. In Camp F. the prisoners overpowered the Russian guards and confiscated the cooking water being transported to the kitchen. The soldiers stormed the cauldrons. At Camp V. the cauldrons steamed in twenty-four-hour shifts and produced a bran soup; every third day a pint and a half of soup for each prisoner. The convoy guarding the soup transport was armed with sticks and iron bars. Anyone who fell sick, died. Later on the organization improved.

Monday, February 1, 1943

In the north pocket, General Strecker's automobile was stolen. Investigation under way. The airdrop marker at S. still illuminated.

The 389th Infantry Division put a combat group to work disposing of corpses through holes in the ice on the Volga.

A pilot reports to the Army Group on having seen signals in

a ravine twenty-five miles west of Stalingrad. Officers assume these come from a group that had broken out. Action cannot be taken on the basis of this uncertain observation.

On the Russian side, artillery and troop concentrations were put into action against the north pocket. From a hilltop Commanders in Chief Voronov and Rokossovski and their staffs observed the movements in the rest of the pocket. This warranted no more than a partial attack.

During the last few days, courts-martial have passed 364 death sentences. The former president of the Supreme Military Court, commanding general in the central pocket, capitulates. Hitler says (after deprecating the surrender of Paulus): "There must be something we can do to make Strecker hold out to the end." A radio message from Supreme Headquarters of the German Army was thereupon dispatched to Strecker, commanding general in the north pocket.

Pleased at their apparently humane treatment, two senior medical officers offered a Russian column commander a cup of coffee. In their eyes it was a crime not to capitulate now. But they refused to urge others to do so.

Field Marshal Milch has now assembled the necessary air force, equipment, and other essentials; he would now be able to fly in massive air supplies.

Tuesday, February 2, 1943

During the night General von Angern talks to the senior medical officer G.; von Angern says he will refuse to surrender. He is later found dead out in the open. When von Angern's staff officers emerge from their cellars in the morning, Germans standing around just have time to call out to them: "Don't shoot!"

General von L. surrendered his division in the O. ravine. What was left of the soldiers lined up in the ravine. Von L. thanked his men and wished them good luck on their uncertain path. Then the Russian commander Rokossovski spoke. The two generals saluted each other, and walked like friends, close together, to a bunker situated higher up, where lunch was served.

Columns of prisoners were led around in a circle for nearly thirty miles; it was said that the available warm bunkers were filled with corpses.

Sections of the 76th Infantry Division—their badge, the old grenadier's hat of the Prussian Guard—surrendered. An exhausted man lies down by a group of corpses. According to the calculations of the Supreme Command's department dealing with enemy armies in the east, the end of hostilities in Stalingrad has released 107 Russian units and thirteen Army Panzer regiments. In actual fact, some of these troops had already left Stalingrad during the final days. The officer in charge of the reconnaissance section of the Russian Don front was replaced because in December and again in January he had wrongly estimated the number of men in the pocket. This number was totally incorrect; General Voronov showed him how the correct figures could have been arrived at on the basis of prisoners' statements.

All captured generals are interrogated singly and in groups by senior Russian officers. Kunowski as quartermaster in chief in the pocket is interrogated separately.

That evening Field Marshal Paulus was brought once more before the Don front staff. Voronov and Rokossovski, who are about to fly to Moscow, present him with the following questions:

1. Were you aware that we were preparing an offensive for November?
   Partially denied.
2. As an intelligent and experienced general, how could you risk such a dangerous operation without adequate flank protection?
   Agreed to their satisfaction, while pointing out existence of orders.
3. Then what did you rely on? Why didn't you display the required activity? You could have tried, couldn't you, to penetrate our front?

Paulus replied that he was unable to decide these matters, such decisions having been made at a higher level.

At this stage Paulus was particularly on edge and exhausted, his left eye twitched. The Russian officers gave up trying to determine the real motives of the Fascist leader. Their intention was:

1. To analyze Paulus's motives.
2. To derive lessons for their own strategy.
3. To convince Paulus of the correctness of Marxist-Leninist leadership by his own personal example.

However, the generals were in a hurry. A sensible interrogation of Paulus was not possible at this time.

World of protocol—
cast of characters

I
What do the soldiers protect?

What do the soldiers protect? The internal order. What is this order? The existing one. Of what does it consist? The organization of the economy. What does this do? The workers serve, the employers serve. Whom do they serve? Church and soldiers. Whom do these serve? Order. Whom does this serve? Church, Army, and the organization of the economy. Who protects it? The soldiers.

II
Historical sketch

> Armies of princes
> Armies of pillage
> Armies of faith
> Frederick the Great's battle order

After the defeat of Jena and Auerstädt, the principle of enlightenment was applied then and then only to the military system in Prussia. Those who are held together by an idea need no battle line. The Prussian reformers adopted the *levée en masse* for the monarchy: an example of the advantage of reform in the nonreformed world; the monarchy now possessed an effective machine for survival.

In 1848 there were still liberals in the Army. It was the Army's function to guarantee the internal order, the throne. In the long run this function excluded liberalism. In 1848 democracy triumphed over the Army; the Army quietly resuscitated. "The Army is now our Fatherland," said Roon. The *coup d'état* followed shortly after the achievement of increased military budgets.

The crisis came in 1918. On July 19, 1918, the Pan-Germans, led by Hugenberg, who were carrying on the war "resigned in spirit from the war." On October 17 General Ludendorff said: "Grip the people, sweep them off their feet, can't Herr Ebert do that? It must be done." On October 27 Ludendorff was dismissed. On November 22 the Supreme Command of the German Army studied a plan to clean up Berlin with ten divisions. Later on that was achieved in somewhat different form. The main thing: to salvage the most important conservative factor—the Army.

Despite its alliance with the government party, the Army melted away. On April 1, 1919, it consisted of 800,000 men; on January 10, 1920, of 400,000. By May 15, 1920, there were only 200,000 men left. On January 1, 1921, the Reichswehr Command reported a personnel of 100,000 (to this must already be added, however, the so-called "secret" Reichswehr).

In 1925 there was a weakening of the Reichswehr; the year 1926 was a bad one for the Reichswehr. During this period the officers' corps and its leaders learned to proceed cautiously and defensively: their objective was to maintain the substance of the Reichswehr.

Hitler's seizure of power saw the Reichswehr as a defense. After reintroducing conscription the Supreme Command trained a defense army until 1939. For defensive reasons, compromises were made between conceptions of defense and attack as well as compromises of a military-political and personnel-political nature: so as to maintain the principle of the Reichswehr. The Army did not want the war. But here, too, it made compromises (including the compromise of the Russian campaign): so as to maintain the substance of the Reichswehr which had been absorbed by the Wehrmacht. Successes made the officers greedy. Nevertheless, for the majority the war in Russia was not their war, it was a compromise: so as to maintain a vital tradition, the unrelinquishable Reichswehr.

III
Genealogy

For the generation of 1830 to 1860, it was that of 1810 to 1840 that made the decisions.

For the generation of 1860 to 1890, it was the preceding one.

For the generation of 1890 to 1920, it was the last but one that made the decisions.

For the generation of 1910 to 1940, it was first the last but two that made the decisions; later on, the last but one did not wish to be pushed aside.

Hitler pushed aside the older generation,
after 1933 and 1940 the young ones
wanted finally
to live
to act
not take a chance again on the older generation
not calculate the risk
(which the older generation was already doing).

Hindenburg knew his grandmother's gardener, who had served two weeks under Frederick the Great. Hindenburg participated in the campaign of 1866; as a lieutenant he was at Versailles. In 1911 he retired. Then he returned to take charge of World War I. In 1917 he celebrated his seventieth birthday. In 1919 he wrote his memoirs. In 1925 he was dug up again as Reich President by the Right. The doctrine he preached was: no adventures. Take away that piece of paper, said Secretary of State Meissner, otherwise the old fellow will sign it. He liked signing his name. In 1934 he succeeded in rescuing twenty-seven conservatives. Actually all he ever wanted was to own the Neudeck estate.

Obligation not to think

In polite society there was a convention not to query the course undertaken. In the same way, at the court of Louis XIV the success or failure of a comedy was decided by the King's laugh. But there was no king in Germany between 1920 and 1930. On the contrary, those who set the tone were in turn dependent on those who looked to them for guidance.

In the summer of 1933 General von Blomberg, Minister of War, refused as an officer to take part in political discussions. Von Bismarck, grandson of the great Bismarck, said he had come to see not von Blomberg the officer but von Blomberg the minister. Von Blomberg banged the table with his fist: "I forbid such talk in my office." Von Bismarck replied: "If Roon had thought like that in 1862, the Democrats would be sitting here now, not you." Between the capacity of German generals to carry on military politics and their tendency to keep entirely aloof from politics as a matter of principle there was a distribution of labor. Cowardice, ambition, intelligence, knowledge, initiative, forthrightness, served one purpose: to promote the Army. Even in von Bismarck's conservative camp, distribution of labor existed: some supported the new course, others offered resistance in a manner reflecting honor on themselves; both served to maintain their class.

IV

... when I see a regiment of German dragoons ride by and observe the beauty and strength of those young men, I derive some comfort again and tell myself that in the long run humanity is not so badly off after all.

J. P. Eckermann, *Conversations with Goethe,*
March 12, 1828.

Hohenfriedberg March

As soon as the mounted military band had reached its position facing the commanding officers' dais, the artillery detachment stationed in H. emerged from a group of trees at the north end of the parade ground at H. and trotted forward. In ranks of four columns and/or gun carriages each, the detachment, whose tradition went back to the combined "Field Artillery Regiment 6" and the "Seydlitz Cuirassiers," paraded past Commander H., who stood saluting on his dais surrounded by guests, officers, ladies, and horsemen of the garrison town of H., which possessed neither industry nor agriculture but lived virtually on the two infantry battalions and the artillery detachment.

Cavalry March No. 16

The cavalry military band corps, led by a drummer on a white horse, emerged from a group of trees near the parade ground at M. and took up position facing the dais. The drummer threw his arms into the air. The mounted squadrons followed, then after 1938 the light reconnaissance vehicles.

Prussian Grenadier March No. 112

Some distance off, the battalions started moving with a flag contingent in the middle. Mounted officers, swords shouldered, lowered when they reached the dais; twenty yards before reaching the dais they changed to goose step: the general, who appeared on horseback with a military entourage, unsheathed his sword, lowered it as soon as the flag contingent had approached to within a certain distance. The horses were fidgety.

"Hoch– und Deutschmeister" March

In white mess jackets at the generals' reunion at the spa of Bad G.: champagne punch is served! Dr., later General, von Hubicky, finds suitable words with which to welcome the new commandant, who waved to the band as it struck up a march potpourri of Austrian and German melodies.

Prussian Infantry March No. 5

Seven battalions, flag contingent, mounted antitank detachment. Shortly afterward the troops fan out for a mock battle. Red light pours over a destroyed tank. It is an enemy tank of the "Reds" (red ribbon around steel helmet), who are put to flight.

Prussian Infantry March No. 6

Heavy tractors with small square engine hoods, all-metal wheels. A gun group gets stuck in the muddy grass near a group of trees. It should never have driven here! The general reviewing the parade curses as he leaves the field.

Entry March of the Guests, from *Tannhäuser*:

No celebration in K. was thinkable unless organized by Chief Medical Officer Dr. M. He was the best speaker in the K. area. He rehearsed the music to be played with the regimental band-master D.

Cavalry March No. 6

St. Barbara's Day! The artillery commander climbs onto the mess table and shouts: "Long live the chase!" The cry is echoed from all sides: "Long live the chase!" He shouts the words himself. Civilians in hunting attire, officers, applaud. Later on (the band switches to Cavalry March No. 4), to the smiles of the commanding officer, the seven youngest officers of the artillery detachment ride up the steps of the building into the mess hall and around the dining table. Champagne is poured, paid for by the civilians.

Gerda von A. was to be paired off with Major G.; the couple balked. First Lieutenant von W. was then supposed to seduce the strait-laced girl, who was a good pianist. It was really extraordinary that she could not find a man. Von W. was successful. Next an attempt was made to couple Gerda von A. with Captain M. in K. When that failed there remained, since marriage with von W. was out of the question, only a marriage of convenience with a brewery owner, a lieutenant of the reserve. The commandant thought the whole thing was a disgrace. As long as this colonel was in command, von W. remained a first lieutenant. The commandant died in southern Russia, his successor knew nothing about the business. Von W. rose as high as colonel. The liaison with von W. had virtually put Gerda von A. out of the running. From 1924 to 1939 the officers of Artillery Detachment 26 in H.

married only rich daughters from the Magdeburg plains. The garrison had the reputation of being wealthy. Captains G., R., K., and W. conspired to make a match between Captain B., who was said to be unsociable, and the garrison commander's daughter. The marriage facilitated B.'s advance; on the other hand, since his wife had no hesitation in betraying him with younger officers, she hampered his advance. Lieutenant von H.'s greeting, when he was introduced in the officers' mess at P., consisted of a short bow, which was not really usual. With the tacit approval of their commanding officer, the first lieutenants of Artillery Regiment 6 wore their uniform jackets an inch and a half longer than was permitted. This fashion fell into disuse after the departure of Lieutenant U. By spring 1942 the reformers in the Army had managed to obtain permission for the troops south of the Loire to wear the top uniform button undone in summer.

Promotions

An officer was judged on the following points:

1. Experience with the troops.
2. Normal career progress, i.e., no obvious favoritism, but then again smooth passage around the awkward headland of major.
3. Reasonable participation in social functions, healthy relationship with fellow officers.
4. Possible interest in riding.
5. Interest in cards on a staff officer level.
6. Possible interest in opera, or other interests indicating intellectual awareness.

Unfavorable: reading books, showing off, excessive affairs with women, theorizing, *novarum rerum cupiditas*, especially in the area of field artillery, fortress artillery, and cavalry: beware of innovations!

The oldest Reichswehr officer was von Rundstedt, later field marshal. Military academy graduates of the years 1904 to 1913 followed in well-defined levels in the commanding positions. For subsequent military academy graduates, promotion was difficult;

it became easy again for graduates after 1936. The expression was: "I was at military academy," not: "I was at the military academy." From 1907 to 1910, the following were at military academy: von Fritsch, von Hammerstein-Equort, von Schleicher, von Harbou, Hoepner, Franz von Papen, von Kluge, von List, von Kleist, von Reichenau, von Weichs, von Wietersheim, among others. Von Manstein, later field marshal, did not enter until 1913. After 1918 the Reichswehr accepted mainly young General Staff officers (captains). The active officers' strata were overlaid by the glut after 1935 and then 1939 and 1940 (teachers, archivists, engineers, lawyers, scientists, economists, etc.). Since 1920 Captain G. had long ranked equally with Captains W., von B., R., and P. Then he overtook them en route to the rank of colonel. In 1936 R. and P. overtook him. They were overtaken by von B., who then caught up with G. But in 1941 R. and P. overtook both so hopelessly that G. no longer regarded them as rivals. He was glad he was always six months senior to von B. Von B. was such an excellent tournament rider that he really ought not to have been sent to the front.

Staying power!
Colonel H. displayed outstanding staying power in the garrison town of Q. During the fall maneuvers of 1936 there was a sudden change in the weather. The officer in charge ordered the exercises discontinued. The treacherous fall weather might entail losses among the men. However, Colonel H., who did not receive the discontinuance order, completed his maneuver exercises near Vienburg; finally he marched with his disheveled soldiers to Q. He did not mention the inclement weather in his report. In December, 1941, Major General F. withdrew his 1942 tanks at Kaliningrad in the cold without having to shoot one of his men to maintain discipline. The rather stocky, purplish man stood personally at the intersections. If it had been merely a matter of leading tanks forward or backward, F. would always have produced optimum results. But even in January, 1941, on receipt of partly contradictory orders, he managed to hold out. He simplified the orders,

some of which were barely intelligible, until they were practicable. The only situation F. could not cope with was when there was no time to "cut through it," i.e., to simplify; what was needed here was staying power. A Panzer division showed excellent staying power when, coming from the Ukraine in the summer of 1942, it got through to Voronezh and captured an important bridge on the way. Even in difficult situations it was necessary to remain calm. The commanding general of the . . . Army Corps sent out patrols to reconnoiter the important river crossing at D. near the Dniester. The order to reconnoiter the river was passed down from division to regiment, to a battalion, to a company, to a platoon, to a reconnaissance patrol. The patrol reported: the river is thirty-three feet wide. The corps requested confirmation. Confirmation followed: the river was between thirty and thirty-three feet wide, not deep. The cautious commanding general requested the regimental commander to check this report personally. According to the corps staff map the river might be wider. The report came back: thirty-one and one-half feet. The corps staff had this figure confirmed by the division. Thereupon the commanding general decided that engineers attached to the corps could be used by the Army elsewhere. When the corps reached the river, it turned out to be some 120 feet wide, with no fords. The commanding general refrained from disciplinary action and remained calm even in this situation. He did not report the discrepancy to his superiors; instead, he tried as quickly as possible to get back the engineers' unit that had been marching off in another direction for several days.

General von K. had the reputation of being especially excitable; telephone operators and staffs were afraid of him. When he was upset, his neck and face in his tight uniform turned purple. Those he was abusing were afraid the general might punish them by dying on the spot. Of General Q. it was said that he was often to be seen at threatened points at the front; he was considered a showoff! General von Wietersheim, as was laid down in the manual for senior officers, remained farther in the rear at corps staff headquarters waiting for the reports that could form a basis for his instructions. Even when no reports came in he remained where he was. Experience taught that at some time or other reports always did come in that could form a basis for his instructions. He refused to drive impatiently to the front lines, there being nothing to see up there. Even when at a certain critical moment in the Polish campaign the somewhat choleric Luftwaffe General von Richthofen requested von Wietersheim to drive up to a river crossing, von Wietersheim refused. Apparently the troops had got stuck there. Von Wietersheim did not let this affect his staying power. As it happened, a few hours later reports from up front came in that allowed von Wietersheim to undertake steps making it possible for the river to be crossed before the day was out.

General von Wietersheim's principles

Someone must always remain outside the disaster situation, i.e., from a somewhat more comfortable command post encourage hopelessly placed captains and men suffering from cold and ammunition shortage; if a company commander loses his nerve, the battalion commander (somewhat better off) would not be far away, and he knows that behind him is the regimental commander. The regimental commander is supervised by the divisional commander and his Ia. If no one else, at least the corps commander is out of the worst and can inspire all the foregoing. The corps commander in turn is supervised by the Army, whose headquarters are far removed from the trouble spot. Should the Army command become involved (as, for example, in the case of Hoth's weak army at Stalingrad), Army Group headquarters would always be there to encourage others and keep its head. These commanders have no business at the front, von Wietersheim used to say. Hence on January 26, 1943, Schmidt, chief of staff of the 6th Army, vented his wrath on Divisional General Leyser of the 29th Motorized Division in the Stalingrad pocket because the latter had spent almost twenty days among the troops at the front. (The fact that Field Marshal von Reichenau often broke the rule by leading a single horse or a battalion forward, and exposing himself to danger in the foremost front lines, is explained as follows: there were enough well-protected Army and other commanders in their headquarters at the rear. The machinery was running. Thus the commander in chief of all the armies could commit symbolic acts and displays of temperament at the front. If the situation had become difficult, von Reichenau would have hurried back and encouraged from the rear.)

Déformation professionelle

Increased power of command reshaped the faces. Reasons: 1. "Keep the men up front." 2. Prestige. 3. Imitation. In this way the highest-ranking generals are to be recognized by their tightly-drawn skin, their pointed, stiffly backward-slanting ears, so-called horsemen's ears. In the Middle Ages women with ears like that were burned. Smooth lips, sharp, snapping eyes, calciferous sharp voice.

Weaknesses and strengths

Major General L. wept one day during an offensive when he saw twenty-seven of his tank crews lost, because the Russians now possessed a Panzer gun that penetrated the German armor plating.

When, after the first years of revival of the Reichswehr, a real parade was permitted again at the conclusion of the fall maneuvers of 1926 near Q., and the troop units placed at various points started to move off with great dependability (as in the old days!) —the effect was almost musical as these varying bodies of men, some of them catching the light, deployed along the side of a slope—General of the Artillery L. began to sob. The officers with him pretended not to notice. In his concluding address L. compared the spectacle of the display with the tragic fate of the dead at Verdun. He criticized the thirst for display and the thirst for organization that had prompted this parade. All the officers were fed up with the way the maneuvers had ended. At dinner in the mess the atmosphere did not improve. If the general had reacted differently they would have taken offense at his sobbing.

Colonel Gallus wept when seventy German tanks unexpectedly

turned up in 1943 a few miles west of where he was holding out, a position that was as good as lost. He had thought he would have to keep his remaining soldiers there without hope. In Stalingrad on January 26 Cavalry Captain von G. wept when three privates of his former, now annihilated, reconnaissance detachment reported to him; without leave they had left a unit to which they had been compulsorily assigned. That same evening the three men captured an enemy-occupied ruin that was threatening the captain's command post. Dr. V. was put in charge of a field hospital in Stalingrad. On January 11, with makeshift assistance, V. had to transfer this field hospital six miles to the east. At L., the new location, V. received orders after two days to go to Stalingrad with his remaining assistants. On the way there V.'s feet were frozen. In Stalingrad no one had any use for him. A chief medical officer assigned him to a cellar casualty station of unattended wounded. Two of V.'s colleagues committed suicide. When fire broke out in the cellar and the whole complex came under artillery fire, Dr. V. crouched among the wounded and wept. "Do be reasonable," said Colonel A. Mencken of the General Staff during a disastrous night of retreat to a young staff officer with the rank of captain who either could not or would not pull himself together. "What kind of reason is that," replied the captain, "which prevents people in a situation like this from simply running away?" No one found out about the incident. Colonel S., one of the last to leave Stalingrad by plane, could not be kept silent by his comrades after his recovery. At semiofficial functions he began to weep; he would make accusations against the higher command that he could not prove. His fellow officers warned him. In the end he was court-martialed.

When during the winter crisis of 1941–1942 Major General, later Colonel General, M. drove to the command post of the . . . Army Corps (only, as it happened, to say hello to an old friend there, since there were no troops under his command in this area), he found the commanding general in tears. This was M.'s first experience of such a thing. The chief of staff active yet helpless.

214

Map appeared saturated with enemy troops; adjutants brought drinks to help restore the exhausted commanding general, almost frozen to death from his drive along the front through the extreme cold. The Ib attempted to get rid of Major General M. outside staff quarters. M. pushed him aside and saw the weeping general. M. reported to Hitler. Needless to say, general and staff were relieved of their posts. General P. was never used again. The officers' club to which he had belonged since World War I expelled him. P.'s weeping had not caused any damage. The general had no opportunity to explain why he was weeping. Major General M., said Colonel General S., did not show enough *sang-froid* here; in one way he had failed to measure up! If M. had arrived an hour later, he would have seen the corps staff at work in the normal way. Losses in old and competent officers were staggering at that time. The corps could really not afford the loss of its experienced staff. What was M. doing, anyway, in A.? said the colonel general. A few days later Colonel General S. was also relieved of his post on grounds of weak behavior.

The officer who showed the greatest staying power in drinking was Major Prittuhn of the . . .th Panzer Division. He could consume brandy until the small hours and then, his face bright red, would drive at the head of his detachment to the maneuver terrain. In Brittany, during the night of June 16–17, 1942, Lieutenants von W., G., and von B., without their commanding officer, had their Panzer detachment go out and shoot at haystacks. The damage had to be paid for out of their own pockets. In 1939 Lieutenant H. drove in a Panzer reconnaissance vehicle from P. to the State Opera House in Berlin to show off his new black Panzer uniform. On the occasion of the Kaiser's birthday, in 1916, the doctors of the . . .th field hospital near Lille, led by Chief Medical Officer von W., got drunk. The next morning von W. could not get up. Drs. H., K., and M. performed a series of operations. During an abdominal operation K., who was administering the anesthetic, vomited; fortunately the incision was already closed. A Catholic head nurse, who was having an affair with one of the doctors, although the affair was coming to an end at that time, reported the incident. The matter was hushed up by the chief medical officer.

Artillery Commander B. could drink two quarts of strong schnapps and sixteen glasses of beer without affecting the clarity of his mind; he could still check and initial gunnery programs.

Jokes

Colonel General S. never again laughed so heartily as he did at the jokes of his chief quartermaster, Lieutenant Colonel von K. After the latter's death there was a gap in the staff. Captain von B. was the buffoon of the . . .th Division. The rather slender man (a horseman's figure) would fire himself, as if he were a gun, at the laugh target, the senior officer at table, and hang on persistently to this target until he made the officer laugh; the other officers, in duty bound to laugh, too, were not always so pleased at B.'s accurate aim. Some of them said he had developed this characteristic for fear of making the wrong impression. From Colonel General M. he received a rebuff. Before the battle of Byelgorod, M. would tolerate neither jokes nor laughter in the 9th Army.

An Army examining judge made a derogatory remark about a well-known division; the remark was passed on to the divisional commander. The latter struck the examining judge in the face with gloves; the judge was relieved of his post.

Comradeship in the forbidden zone

When General von Schleicher (1st Foot Guard Regiment, member of the General Staff, head of the Ministry Department, Minister of the Reichswehr, etc.) was to be shot, no one helped him (the man who had helped so many into the saddle, who had stood behind so many). His friend von Bredow (1st Foot Guard Regiment, holder of the Pour-le-Mérite, member of the General Staff, etc.) was shot the same day. Friends of von Bredow and von Schleicher attempted to call up the deputy Commander in

Chief of the Army or the Chief of General Staff to ask for help; the commanders could not be reached: in cases of conflict where a commander cannot or may not act (or, according to circumstances, despite tragic conflicts may not wish to act), but yet who, once he has been informed, would have to act honorably, the commander had to remain inaccessible. The case of Colonel General von Fritsch concerned an alleged morals offense. Chief of General Staff Beck helped von Fritsch to the extent of stationing a company of soldiers in the vicinity of the alleged crime where von Fritsch was being examined by the state police; if von Fritsch had actually been threatened, the company would have fired. These orders were given by Colonel General Beck, whom no one helped when he was dismissed by Hitler. At the end of December, 1941, the successful Colonel Generals Guderian and Hoepner had no hesitation in retreating with the tanks with which they had been left in a hopeless position in the cold. They had previously requested orders; Chief of General Staff Halder, when Hoepner put through an urgent telephone call, instructed his adjutant to say he was not there; he, too, was afraid of Hitler. Shortly afterward, Field Marshal von Kluge was given command of the Central Army Group. During three campaigns he had been annoyed at insubordinate tank commanders, who were not properly under his command or at least did not obey him. Now he helped to get them thrown out of their jobs. He received Hoepner and shut himself up with him in his office for two hours; Kluge informed Hoepner that the Führer had dismissed him, Hoepner, and had deprived him of rank, decorations, and pension. He advised Hoepner to shoot himself. Hoepner did not do this. The unfortunate General Stumme, whose subordinate had a subordinate who lost important General Staff plans involving Russian territory, was compensated for his dismissal by being invited by von Bock to sit at his right one evening at dinner; friends subsequently helped him get to Africa, where he was soon killed. When the Chief of the General Staff himself, Colonel General Halder, had to go, no one moved a finger for him, although all the senior officers discussed the affair among themselves.

Demotions

Dismissed or died within six months during 1941, Field Marshal von Rundstedt, Field Marshal von Reichenau, Field Marshal von Leeb, Field Marshal von Bock, Field Marshal von Witzleben, Field Marshal von List, Field Marshal von Brauchitsch, Colonel Generals Ritter, von Schobert, Hoepner, Guderian, Strauss, etc. Except for two, all were of the old school. Von Kluge, middle line between "reformers" and "old school," wanted to survive whatever happened. He did survive the end of most of the reformers but died two years later.

In the winter of 1941 Field Marshal von Brauchitsch was still in office; he visited Field Marshal von Bock in Smolensk. It was freezing cold. Streets and sidewalks were slippery. Getting out of his official car, Brauchitsch fell on the ice. Von Bock, who had come out from his quarters to greet him, tried to help him; in doing so he fell himself. Within a few weeks both field marshals had lost their posts.

Can the world of protocol carry out a putsch?

1. The old school tries

In 1933 von Hammerstein-Equort and von Stülpnagel wanted possibly to try something; in 1938 Halder and von Brauchitsch, together with some other generals, wanted perhaps to try something.

In 1939 it was said that von Hammerstein-Equort, then in Cologne, was possibly going to try something.

From 1939 to 1942 the generals were on the whole successful; successful generals do not carry out a putsch.

In 1943 von Kluge wanted perhaps to try something; he was known as a fast driver. When he made his lightning visits by car to the front, he instructed the drivers to go as fast as they could. Plans to assassinate Hitler, in which he intended to take part, were interrupted by his being involved in a serious car accident. Field Marshal von Witzleben had to undergo an operation for hemorrhoids before he could implement a putsch plan; while he was in hospital, Hitler relieved him of his post. Von Manstein, when he could show strategic successes, had no plans for opposition. When he did want to oppose, he never had any successes to show at that moment; but in 1943 not many senior commanders had striking successes; unsuccessful generals cannot carry out a putsch.

2. Corruption from above

> Acquired during the war with God's
> gentle blessing.
>
> General von H.'s fortune,
> Thirty Years' War.

On his retirement, Colonel General Zeitzler could have chosen between a country estate, money, or a high decoration; although annoyed, Hitler was prepared to make some presentation; Zeitzler refused parting gifts as being corruption from above. On the other hand, Field Marshal von Kluge accepted a check for Reichsmarks 250,000 from Hitler on his birthday; he was allowed to invest Reichsmarks 125,000 of this in his estate. Field Marshals von Manstein, von Bock, and Busch (as well as other fellow officers) also accepted gifts. In 1944 von Manstein tried to buy a suitable country estate first in Silesia and then in Pomerania. In duty bound von Manstein was at that time still counting on a draw in the over-all war situation. In view of the certainty of imminent German defeat, Field Marshal von Bock, who had likewise accepted a gift, was to have the whole situation outlined to him in confidence. Von Bock interrupted the officer as soon as he threatened to become critical of the Supreme Command, and shouted: "I will not tolerate any criticism of the Führer. I intend to stand in front of the Führer and defend him against anyone who dares attack him." Hitler appointed Field Marshal Busch, later commander in chief of the Central Army Group, a member of a People's Court. Since he understood nothing of legal matters, he said, he intended to pass death sentences on all the accused. And this, he went on, is what he did, even when the lawyers in the chamber were of a different opinion.

3. The younger generation tries

The happy-go-lucky, often amusing Lieutenant General Stieff, later killed by Hitler, received a conspiratorial letter from General von Treskow and, after tearing it across, would have thrown it into a wastepaper basket at the Führer's headquarters. Lieutenant Colonel von Boeselager, holder of the highest decorations for bravery, wanted to be transferred with his regiment to East Prussia and pounce on Hitler. Officers of von Kluge's staff conspired to undertake a joint pistol attack on Hitler when he came to visit Army Group headquarters. What was to happen after the sixteen pistol shots? Soldiers must always trust to luck. A package of explosives, the size of two bottles of cognac, was placed in the plane in which Hitler was to fly from Smolensk to Rastenburg. The charge did not go off; the package was picked up a few days later at the Führer's headquarters by one of the conspirators. First Lieutenant Schulze-Boysen of the Air Ministry, an idealist, transmitted secret material to the Russians by radio. He and his friends, many of them women, were shot. Von der Bussche wanted to wrap explosives around his body and embrace Hitler in a death grip while demonstrating uniforms; since the uniform supplies to be displayed were bombed, the demonstration did not take place. Von der Bussche had already prepared himself mentally for death. A few weeks later, on the eastern front, he suffered wounds similar to those for which he had been prepared. English explosives that had been hidden by Lieutenant General Stieff under a wooden platform at the Führer's headquarters exploded. Luckily the investigation was in the hands of one of the conspirators. In Vienna the putsch against Hitler was not only carried through to completion (as it was in Paris): subsequently, by general consensus, it was canceled; nothing could be proved. All that happened was that the officer in charge of the counterintelligence office in Vienna, Colonel Count Marogna-Redwitz, who covered up for all the others, was arrested and killed. During a hearing on one of the upper floors of the Chief Reich Security Office, von P. found himself in such a tight spot that he pushed his interrogators away with thrusts and kicks and jumped out of the window. Other arrested officers also betrayed nothing. First Lieutenant G. intended to liberate Count Hardenberg, who was in a Berlin hospital surrounded by guards, with machine pistols that he carried with him across Berlin. On the other hand, he was planning to throw bombs from an airplane onto the Führer's headquarters. When he still had a tank company, he wanted to drive reconnaissance for a possible revolt; he had formerly been a National Socialist. In April, 1945, he was executed.

Seating and greeting protocol

Informal snack often standing; to the left of the commander in chief the IIa or interpreter, behind him the accompanying officers ("like servants"); at a convenient distance the chief of staff as well as Ia and OI. The right side of the commander in chief is reserved for possible guests. It makes no difference whether the snack is taken in the field or indoors. It is always informal.

Mess evening, with guests: horseshoe table. As far as possible, guests on the right of the commander in chief or highest-ranking officer. Horseshoe sections for those accompanying the guests. Chief of Staff, Ia, IIa, IIb, Ib, Ic, seated; adjutants and accompanying officers standing.

In the garrison town of F. it happened that . . . ; when General Stumme was relieved of his command by Hitler, Field Marshal von Bock had this lower-ranking officer sit on his right at Poltava; this affront to Hitler went the rounds of the armies of the Southern Army Group.

The equal-ranking Generals X. and F. . . . . The first to arrive at the village of S. in the southern Ukraine was the divisional commander L.; shortly afterward the divisional commander von B., who was senior to him in terms of years of service, arrived in the same village. Who was to have priority at the dinner table (in one of the larger rooms of a cottage)?

At conferences, the following may lean on the map table with one or both hands: commander in chief, chief of staff, equal- and higher-ranking participants. At the Führer's headquarters, apart from Hitler: the speaker of the moment, possibly a field marshal or any commander who was present. At briefings on the situation or other subjects, do not read remarks, speak off the cuff!

A perennially touchy question was how to avoid the confrontation of generals who had quarreled. During the retreats in the winter of 1941, the . . . Corps of General D. came onto the retreat route of the neighboring . . . Corps under General F. On reaching the road General D. had the congested highway closed off by his accompanying officers and military police and let his own units go through first. Since that time the two generals were enemies. During a conference of senior commanders in Salzburg, it was barely possible to prevent the two generals meeting in a room.

Written forms of address: If the commander in chief says "Dear Schmidt," General Schmidt must reply "Dear Field Marshal" (or "Lieutenant General"). The commander in chief may say "Kindest regards"; the lower-ranking general may not say this, he says "Yours respectfully." Lower to higher ranks conclude with "Yours obediently," "Yours respectfully," or "Always your obedient"; if the relationship is a more personal one: "In respectful gratitude I am, General, yours sincerely."

Higher to lower ranks conclude with "Yours truly" or, to indicate a personal relationship, "Yours sincerely," or "Yours ever sincerely"; occasionally "Ever yours." However, this eliminates the desired impersonal note. "Best regards" is not common.

Faux pas: "Best wishes" and "Heil Hitler." Correct: "Yours sincerely" or "Yours truly." In correspondence with Hitler: "Heil, my Führer." Reports and letters should not start off with "I." Correct: "It is respectfully reported that," or, "In assessing the situation I wish to report the following," or, "In view of the situa-tion, request leave to report."

While still in command, Colonel General von Seeckt spent his evenings hunting for superfluous words that could be deleted from staff drafts. An order to be signed by Colonel General Adam or by the last of the great stylists among the chiefs of staff, Colonel General Beck, was originally drafted by six officers, then edited for style by four officers, scrutinized by the deputy chief of staff, re-edited, and finally entrusted to the chief of staff himself, who kept finding still simpler, more trenchant abbreviations or expres-sions. The officers of the Count Schlieffen school learned the mental precision work needed to conquer the enemy in the com-position of texts, for here, as in actual warfare, the simpler, shorter, more trenchant measure was the effective one.

On one occasion a draft order was submitted to Field Marshal von Brauchitsch that contained the phrase "under no circumstances whatsoever." The field marshal pointed out to his entourage that this simply was not the kind of language to be used in draft orders. According to him, the following were to be avoided:

Words of foreign origin, always superfluous.

Word repetitions.

Starting orders with "I."

The generals of Old Prussia, Blücher, etc., were quite unable to employ precise language. Hitler flooded those he was talking to with words that had the penetrating effect of water (i.e., depend-ing on the resistance). His military aides of the Schlieffen school, von Ludendorff, von Seeckt, Adam, Beck, and Halder, on the other hand, were skillful in the use of language; even the phrase-ology of the Wehrmacht reports had its roots in their general staff precision. An order of Moltke the elder's would have revealed extraneous terms and phrases. This obstacle had been cut out by the language simplifiers. This irritated Hitler. "It has no content," he said of one of von Kluge's memoranda. "Don't understand it," he said when a report of von Manstein's was submitted to him.

R., later a colonel general, never made a mistake when speaking.

The officers could often not follow his rapid delivery, so pre-occupied were they waiting for a slip of the tongue or a miscon-strued sentence, but the words always came out in the right order. On the other hand, General of the Infantry Strecker was unable to complete a sentence, he threw fragments of sentences into the conversation. ("Say, listen, here, up here, up along here, gentlemen; listen, that's something I'd like to see!" or: "Go on, hurry up, keep going! Hurry up, keep going, hurry up, hurry up!" or: "Let's go!") Sodenstern and Greiffenberg, chiefs of staff of Army Groups A and B, spoke fluently, although when they were overtired they might make a slip on the telephone. Problems arose between two generals who were articulate and a superior com-mander who had difficulty expressing himself. Those who could express themselves were at a disadvantage; they were regarded as snobs. The important thing was to throw your heart over the hurdle, said von Manstein to Hitler, who was a passionate non-rider and rejected von Manstein's proposal.

An official casualty list of the various battles fought by Hanni-bal, Caesar, Napoleon, etc., was submitted to Field Marshal Count Schlieffen. Schlieffen's eye was caught by the losses at Borodino which, with 48,000 French and 56,000 Russians, were remarkably high. Not bad! said the field marshal.

Schlieffen as model: be more than you seem

Schlieffen, chair in the shade; the speaker, i.e., the subordinate, sitting in the light; without saying a word Schlieffen listened. No one was entitled to ask him a question; he was always entitled to embarrass others by asking questions. Tremendous knowledge of military personnel and detail, despite shortsightedness obliging him to wear a monocle.

Leadership technique: question—answer; if the answer is wrong, another question follows that can be very embarrassing. In Schlief-fen's case, for instance, whenever chiefs of staff mispronounce the names of Southwest African tribal chiefs. (He received reports on the operations in German Southwest Africa three times a day.) Schlieffen kept abreast of progress in the Berlin military academy by attending lectures. Even on his daughter's wedding day he wanted to hear about German Southwest Africa.

Unfortunately the only war actions of his day were the Boxer Rebellion in China—Schlieffen supervised the countermeasures from the Wilhelmshöhe Palace—and the Hottentot war in German Southwest Africa.

Even on his last general staff inspection trip, on the verge of old age, he was plotting three war situations simultaneously, each on a major scale. At that time every first lieutenant from his school knew how to win campaigns in France.

Brilliant victory. But what is brilliant about a victory? Schlieffen said: "The way of retreat is usually dusty or wet. Efforts to prevent the enemy escaping are never brilliant; those involved are often so tired they don't bother to look."

V
Von Reichenau's Army

The 6th Army was General von Reichenau's; it had originally been the 10th Army. This army, formed in Leipzig, was regarded as a particularly brilliant one. It was better equipped than other armies. Its commander, General von Reichenau, was considered capable, a National Socialist. Hindenburg regarded him as frivolous. Von Reichenau always drove his Mercedes compressor himself. He wore a monocle in his right eye. There was a gap between his center incisor teeth; his face was florid, often purplish, his neck compressed in a rather too tight uniform collar.

Unsentimental;

full, uninhibited *joie de vivre*;

lively posing in front of his troops;

a Reichswehr general who talks politics, a military leader who cannot be reached for some hours because he is leading a solitary horse by the bridle over a bad stretch of road; on another occasion he is leading a solitary battalion for two or three miles forward across some meadows;

makes a point of wearing field uniform, forage cap instead of dress cap;

in 1934 composed press directives after the execution of his predecessors, Generals von Schleicher and von Bredow; the execution might not have taken place if von Reichenau had not failed to act;

in 1935 he composed the Wehrmacht's oath of allegiance to the Führer;

interested in news, interested in the new;

needs company;

the last to stop drinking in the officers' mess.

Von Reichenau, heavy thighed, baggy riding breeches, related to the Bohemian aristocracy, but a man who no longer believed in the vocation of his upper class. No roots in landed estates, no sentimental feeling for the old warrior caste. His native land is his own life and the life of comradeship; hence total freedom of movement in this world; von Reichenau vis-à-vis this world: like a robber baron and his followers. The pose is therefore permissible; no reason to refrain from pleasure since no reason for puritanism; hence not confined to any existing military niche; largely free to wear a highly personal mask: for example, subordinates can address him directly, capricious in his degree of aloofness. He used to say he would like to see officers and men calling each other by first names. Not disconcerted by presence of superiors, smokes cigarettes during meals; reckless in the face of enemy fire, which cannot be estimated anyway: chief danger is not the loss of one's own existence (since existence has almost no independent meaning); chief characteristic: strongly determined by sympathies, cold. When Himmler, Heydrich, and Daluege of the police approached von Reichenau's table at a hotel, von Reichenau, without getting up, merely said: Join us, but don't disturb us!

Has he been filmed?

He was always being filmed.

Favorite weapons: pistols, artillery. As a young man he accompanied his father, General von Reichenau (retired) to South America to sell Ruhr artillery.

Attitude to National Socialism: he had confidence in a movement, committed himself to it, and wanted a hand in controlling it, the experts said it made tools of men; he took it for granted he was by no means a tool, this movement must be properly influenced by him.

Attitude to cadet types: in France, Colonel General von Bock, von Reichenau's superior, wanted to achieve victory two weeks earlier than von Reichenau. Von Reichenau's policy of caution prevailed. At the start of the 1941 winter, von Bock drove his overtaxed armies toward Moscow. Von Reichenau halted the 6th Army. Adventure demands audacity. But it doesn't say what audacity. Cadets, said von Reichenau, understand nothing about adventures, but neither about nonadventures.

In the Polish campaign, von Reichenau's creature, the Army, coming from Silesia, was successfully swung north and closed off important pockets. During the winter of 1939–1940 von Reichenau had men of the 6th Army shot to improve discipline. In the west the Army pushed into Belgium, executed important battles. The Army was earmarked for the landing in England. The capture of Gibraltar was to be assigned to it. Later the Army found itself on the northern flank of the Southern Army Group in southern Russia. Here, too, it was reputed to be magnificently equipped. A year later, facing Stalingrad, the Army had as many divisions as would otherwise be shared by two armies.

In January, 1941, von Reichenau was given command over the Southern Army Group; he retained his Army. In Poltava this energetic man was now in charge of two large staffs. This was the kind of thing he had always been striving for. From the very beginning he had been a Reichwehr man; from the outset he had been a follower of Hitler. Until then fellow officers had hindered von Reichenau's promotion. The crisis in the command at Christmas, 1941, deprived these fellow officers of power. Von Reichenau occupied his new post for three weeks. One frosty morning, which he began with a run before breakfast, he felt unwell. At the mess he finished his soup; he signed whatever the chief military court counselor put before him. His red table wine remained untouched. In the lobby of the mess, where he tried to pull himself together, von Reichenau suffered a stroke. His brother officers tried to put the heavy, unconscious man into an armchair, tying him firmly to it. They then carried the armchair to an airplane that was to take the field marshal to German soil. En route, while landing in Lemberg, the plane crashed. Von Reichenau received serious head wounds; his field marshal's baton was broken in two. There was a state funeral in Berlin.

Von Reichenau's successor was his former chief of staff, General Paulus. To this day the Russians still call him von Paulus, an analogy to Generals von Rundstedt, von Bock, von Leeb, and their successors von Kückler, von Kluge, and von Reichenau (not forgetting von Manstein, von Kleist, and von List. Not until 1934–1944 did commoners occupy the highest posts).

VI

If someone asks how all these things could have happened, the answer is bound to be: The German officer has grown up in the tradition of obedience. No army can do without it.

Official instruction

Did General Paulus have strong misgivings about the task set his army?

He had doubts.

What was General Paulus like?

Toward the end, physically broken, physically exhausted, quince-yellow. Inclined to be depressed.

Burdened by events.

Had it been a grave mistake of personnel politics to entrust the 6th Army to Paulus?

General Heim says: Yes.

Relationship of Field Marshal von Reichenau to his successor Paulus: since they had shared some outstanding successes in 1939 and 1940, von Reichenau would have favored any promotion of Paulus. Von Reichenau's attitude was: should Paulus be too pedantic in his command, he, von Reichenau, would always be there as Commander in Chief of the Army Group!

Paulus's last troop command had been of a motor-vehicle detachment in Wünsdorf in 1934, otherwise in staffs. His last rank had been general of the Panzer Troops;

preference for driving in Panzer reconnaissance vehicles;

motor goggles, leather coat, tall;

no one would have thought he would become von Reichenau's successor.

Sensitive.

Paulus's chief of staff, Arthur Schmidt, dominated him;

Paulus: generous, circumspect;

orders the release of Russian prisoners from the pocket, the order is not carried out.

Zeitzler: Paulus is doing very nicely.

Heavy cigarette smoker; fine surgeon's hands. He felt let down (a) by the Army Group, (b) by the Luftwaffe, (c) by the Supreme Command of the Army, (d) by Hitler, (e) by his own Army.

Popular.

Punctual.

Always smartly turned out; although toward the end in a sack-like topcoat with baggy pockets, belt just below chest level, in need of protection despite leonine, drawn-down mouth, suffering from colds and gastric ailments.

Always rather embarrassed when he had to have his picture taken outdoors; he often watched planes then.

He was always popular among all his superiors.

Circumspect.

On November 19 Paulus tried to persuade himself it was merely another test like Charkov. He decided to show calmness. On the 20th he called off patrol activity in Stalingrad. On the 21st he reviewed the gravity of the position: tanks in front of his command post; he tried to gain time; he filled up the time with telephone calls. On the morning of the 22nd he met General Hoth. At 2 P.M. he flew into the pocket. On the 23rd he became convinced the Army should break out toward the west. This view was shared by all generals, his chief of staff, the superior chief of staff, the latter's superior commander, and the Chief of the General Staff of the German Army. However, this view did not prevail.

From the 24th on, pocket existence.

Could Paulus hope to get away with leading his Army away from Stalingrad on his own initiative?

Not after November 24, as orders were issued that day.

Before?

Perhaps, perhaps not; it might have been said he should have waited for orders.

Would von Manstein have backed him up?

That is not certain.

Would he have been able to back him up?

That is not certain.

Would Zeitzler have backed him up?

If von Manstein had backed him up, Zeitzler might have backed him up, too. Possibly other field marshals might have spoken in favor of a mild punishment for Paulus.

Paulus

Friedrich Ernst Paulus, born 1890 in Breitenau, Hesse, son of a bookkeeper in a correctional institute; Protestant; ancestors: farmers, dairy managers, teachers, one pastor, prison employees. "His mother had been a beautiful, quiet, patient woman, who knew how to endure much toil and trouble without complaint." General staff officer of the old school, anxious to avoid making an enemy of anyone, painstakingly careful of his appearance, horseman's figure, regardless of what he ate, excessively modest; excellent manners, at his desk a slow, careful worker. He could spend hours composing the wording of an order.

Married a Rumanian aristocrat whose family goes back to the Byzantine emperors.

On combat days, in the evening, he would go through the events of the day in an undertone. In 1922 his company did better than Rommel's at athletic meets and rifle competitions.

Helpless, defenseless, in the face of bad manners; brutal language that disregarded convention paralyzed him. Paulus's faith was not a blind faith, it was faith in convention. In his eyes Hitler was the "Führer," and he had a particularly high regard for his superior, Fritsch; von Reichenau he respected because he was his superior (whether the latter smacked his lips over his soup, fired pistols, or ordered men shot). He also admired his superior von Manstein. When professional differences arose between his superiors Hoepner and Beck he tried to mediate; to his superior Halder he was a loyal and talented disciple.

Self-denial

He did not impose his will on anyone, not even on his Chief of Staff Schmidt, not even on his Army. In the pocket he ate no more than the ration: two and one-half ounces of bread, little else. He did not even demand a room to himself but shared one with his Chief of Staff Schmidt. Nor did he make any effort to be flown out of the pocket. He had not striven for his high post. He was not tempted to envy his rival Seydlitz; he refrained from punishing this opponent. He denied himself an over-all view of the situation as a whole. In September, 1940, he had been entrusted with working out plans for the invasion of Russia. Although he believed the war would be decided in the Near East, he considered it his duty to work out plans for the invasion. Despite qualms as to a breach of confidence, Paulus discussed the invasion plans with his aristocratic wife: he said he could not judge matters of political decision, but important military factors favored an eastern invasion, and at least the early stages would go well.

Not given to panic

A military leader of whom his superior commander knows that he will yield to pressure from the front will not be given any backing by his superiors in a real emergency. Hence in quiet times the military leader must show tenacity, must, so to speak, hoard a reputation in order to ensure being permitted to retreat in an emergency. But what are quiet times? Paulus's behavior at Charkov in 1942, right after taking over the 6th Army, was compared with that of Moltke the elder; Paulus calmly stood his ground in defeat, awaiting the planned approach of the neighboring army; he behaved in this way because the Supreme Command of the German Army had issued orders to wait quietly.

Doubts

He had doubts as to the favorable outcome of the war, but this does not imply that he lapsed into infinite pessimism; he was not a National Socialist, but neither was he an anti-National Socialist; Paulus was annoyed because General Jodl yawned while Paulus was speaking, but he dared not mention it to Jodl; he complained to Colonel von Lossberg instead. On another occasion Colonel von Lossberg said: "Von Manstein must replace von Brauchitsch." Ideas of that kind were beyond the competence of his position, replied Paulus. Nervous twitching on the left side of his face, at times. Paulus: "On orders of the Chief of the General Staff, before the war with Russia broke out I plotted the whole maneuver and put down in writing exactly what would happen. Over there in that safe it is all down on paper. I wonder whether, when I have time, I will finally catch up on my sleep or have a look at what I wrote? I believe it'll be the latter." Not the face of an ascetic, not severe enough for that, but possibly a martyr. When a subordinate of his subordinate General "Panzer" Stumme lost the plans for the summer offensive over the Russian lines in 1942 —as a result of which Stumme was to resign his command— Paulus wanted to submit to a court-martial himself; his superiors prevented him.

In praise of thoroughness

A staff medical officer of the 6th Army laid charges against a private who had reported with a foot injury; the staff doctor proves that there is nothing wrong with the foot. The commander brings the soldier before a court-martial. The military judge sentences him to death. Before signing the sentence, Paulus has the soldier's foot X-rayed. A bone fracture is revealed.

Ideas of duty

The leap in one generation from prison employees and bookkeepers to the big-timers was made at the cost of some difficulty. Paulus acts out many ideals. Personally he adheres to all conventions—conventions set by all the powers known to him: the rules of aristocratic society (generosity, refinement), the rules of his background (punctuality, accuracy), the rules of the old school (soldierly ideals), the rules of the younger generation (tanks), the National Socialist rules (faith). He takes it for granted that the rules are valid. Paulus died after being released from a prisoner-of-war camp the very day (February 2) Hitler would have assumed he would die.

Paulus's assistant

Major General Schmidt, chief of staff of the 6th Army, had a habit, like Frederick II and Frederick William IV, like von Seydlitz and Adam, of arbitrarily changing the subject when talking to inferiors. From the situation in the pocket he jumped (to show how calm he was) to conditions in the riding academy at Hanover, from there back to reminiscences of the year 1936. Wasn't your father, he would ask suddenly, at military academy in Danzig in 1916? Yes, the subordinate would reply. Then the chief of staff jumped back to operational details. The subordinate followed him. But what could the chief of staff have asked in a situation with which he himself was unable to cope?

Schmidt, a bachelor, liked good food, liked a drink, was quick to take offense. Field Marshal von Bock got him his position with the 6th Army, which he was supposed to tighten up. Before Christmas Schmidt said: "We can hold out till Easter." To an officer who was complaining that his men had no weapons, he said: "Well, use your teeth then." In the final stage he organized a smooth surrender for himself and Paulus.

Von Manstein: Schmidt was the stronger personality.

Major von Anders of the General Staff: Compared with Chief of Staff Schmidt, an ordinary major general or lieutenant general was a nobody.

Colonel van Hooven: The Army Group put Schmidt off with incomplete information.

Von Halder: We used to call him Schmidty because he was so short.

Von K.: Schmidt was extraordinarily healthy; I would say, disgustingly healthy.

Schmidt's attitude was that the High Command had brought the Army to Stalingrad, and now it was up to the High Command to get it out of there without the necessity for such a colossal risk as a breakout.

Motivation of the superior officer: von Manstein

"Don't look at me so angrily," said von Manstein to an officer, "I'm only here to straighten things out. I'm not responsible for them." Von Manstein could not prevent the breakout from the pocket from not taking place. He dispatched Major E. to Paulus to encourage him secretly to break out. Although von Manstein forbade the breakout on December 23, he might (had it taken place) have covered up for it—certainly he desired it and did not inwardly disapprove. Paulus did not know that. Von Manstein wanted to prevent the final carnage in the pocket after January 20. When Lieutenant Colonel von Zitzewitz flew out of the pocket and called on von Manstein, the latter told him this but asked him to treat it confidentially. When von Manstein achieved nothing he did not resign: neither after the forbidden breakout at Christmas nor on a later occasion. He forced himself to stay. His fellow officers asked him to stay. Later he was asked to overthrow Hitler as Supreme Commander of the German Army. Von Manstein indicated his plans for an overthrow to a group of confidants, thus betraying himself to Hitler, and although he was very determined he was prevented from taking any extreme step.

Fritz E. von Lewinsky, later on von Manstein, born in 1878,

Plön cadet corps, then: central cadet school at Grosslichterfelde, military academy, class of 1913; in the fall of 1942 von Manstein found himself in the midst of an exciting career.

His call to the Crimea had come very unexpectedly one evening, the news of his promotion to Army Supreme Commander came when he was about to go for a swim in a pond in the forest with his staff officers. In 1942 he became the youngest German field marshal. Hitler had used von Manstein's ideas to launch the western campaign. Under no circumstances did von Manstein want to jeopardize this beginning.

Von Manstein's evasions: In December, General Zeitzler hoped that von Manstein, as the responsible Supreme Commander of the Army Group, could dissuade Hitler from holding Stalingrad. Von Manstein did not want to go to the Führer's headquarters. He did not go until Zeitzler ordered him to do so, and he went directly to Hitler. Zeitzler, who had wanted to speak to von Manstein first, missed him at the airfield; when he asked about the conversation between Hitler and von Manstein, the latter replied: "I'm no match for Hitler's powers of persuasion." Two weeks later von Manstein said to Zeitzler over the phone: "Well, there's one thing I want to say to you, tell the boss he can do what he likes with his corporal's World War I experiences, he's not going to get very far with them here. The day is coming when the men in the pocket are going to get fed up and say, We've had enough. They've been fighting not just for a year but for years, you can't fool them any more. You can go ahead and tell him so quite frankly." Zeitzler answered: "Tell him yourself." Von Manstein: "You can't do that over the phone."

Paulus's case

Didn't von Manstein actually assume responsibility for Stalingrad? Von Manstein would have been prepared to assume responsibility if Paulus had been successful.

Why didn't he see that his order "Winter thunderstorm" was carried out on December 23?

He refrained from insisting that orders be carried out as if he were the executor of an estate. Things had gone wrong without his being to blame. One of von Manstein's General Staff officers put it this way: We did not vote for that criminal Hitler. Von Manstein said: "I never promised anything." He chose his victories in such a way that he could achieve them. Where victories could not be forced, he did not look for them.

Motivation of the superior officer: Zeitzler

During his General Staff training at Münster, Zeitzler already had the reputation of being talented, resourceful, tough, expert, brutal.

Zeitzler, of the younger school of Panzer generals, stocky, was nicknamed Ball of Lightning. Before his appointment as Chief of the General Staff of the German Army he was chief of staff of a Panzer corps and chief of staff in France; there he improvised the defense against the British Dieppe thrust. A wave of confidence bore Zeitzler along during his initial period as Chief of the General Staff.

A General Staff officer of the old school would have taken precautionary measures, covered himself, in his behavior toward Hitler. Zeitzler threw himself avidly into his new task. He put himself completely in Hitler's hands in order to make all the more certain that Hitler would back up the General Staff's reasoned judgment.

On his return on November 23, Hitler said to Zeitzler, who was deeply concerned about the situation in Stalingrad: "Don't let it worry you. We must stand fast when misfortune strikes!" He shook hands with Zeitzler and said: "Thank you. You have done everything humanly possible. Even if I had been there I could have done no more!" There was no time to express misgivings. Zeitzler requested at least a private interview for the following night. During this conversation Zeitzler tried to persuade the Führer, surrounding him with his thoughts. The interview continued until morning. Hitler said: "Reich Marshal Göring has said he will keep the 6th Army supplied by air." Zeitzler said: "Rubbish!" Hitler said: "I will not abandon the Volga!" Zeitzler shouted: "My Führer! The loss of this great army would mean that the spine of the eastern front is broken." The following day they made up again.

In January, Zeitzler and his immediate staff put themselves on pocket rations; Hitler forbade such experiments as impairing the staff's working capacity.

Zeitzler did what he could for the relief of Stalingrad. Two divisions he wanted to send had to be put at the disposal of the weak Rumanians in the Don bend. Half a mountain infantry division was taken from him by Army Group A, half was kept back by the Central Army Group during transit on account of a local crisis. Instead, Zeitzler obtained a promise of western divisions from the Supreme Command for February. His brokering activities gained him constantly shifting ground.

Air supply

> Radio message, February 2, 1943, 1900 hours:
> Five planes have returned from duty.
> The first three planes saw nothing.
> The fourth plane thought it saw something.
> The fifth plane observed lights.

During the first stage, the air supply started out from a distance of 120 miles, during the second from a distance of 180 miles with detours, during the third from a distance of 270 miles. An average of 94.16 tons was transported daily. The peak was reached between December 13 and 21 with an average of 137.7 tons. Some of the planes came from Africa. The transportation of old newspapers, roofing paper, pocketbooks, ties, army-issue condoms, spices, was stopped forthwith. What was lacking was heating equipment, the weather was unfavorable. In mid-January Field Marshal Milch, Secretary of State for the Air Ministry, assumed personal command of the organization. On January 16 he arrived in south Taganrog. On January 17 his car drove into a locomotive near Salk. Milch, still feeling the effects of the accident, telephoned Jeschonnek, Paulus, the Führer, Göring, and five Luftwaffe generals. On January 18 he called on Field Marshal von Manstein to discuss extraordinary measures. On the 19th Milch overcame numerous difficulties. On the 20th the fighter planes and bombers ordered by Milch were in Krakow. The emergency airfield at Gumrak in Stalingrad was gone. On the 24th Milch could lay hands on 308 Junkers 52's, 355 Heinkel 111's, and five large Focke-Wulf 200's. Milch threatened a court-martial, promised rewards. On January 27 the fighters and bombers arrived at Rovenki, i.e., they were now close to Milch. There was no longer an airfield in Stalingrad, but an adequate air supply would actually soon have been possible now.

Preparations for the air supply suffered from faulty information: the task was not a traditional army one. Approximately 250,000 men needed 306 tons of food a day if each man was to receive two pounds eleven ounces. Approximately 1,800 guns firing ten sixty-six pound shells daily needed 540 tons. Approximately 10,000 motors, some of them not in use, at two and one-half gallons a day, needed 100 tons. The necessary volume of supply therefore amounted to between 900 and 1,200 tons.

The Army Command wanted to please its superiors. It asked for 500 tons a day. It received barely 100 tons. So the Luftwaffe was not entirely to blame either.

Then who was to blame for Stalingrad?

General Doerr said: "I believe there was only one person to blame for Stalingrad, and that was that atheist Hitler."

In other words, from a military point of view was everything done as it should be?

From a purely military point of view, everything that was done was done as it should be.

VII
How much did Hitler know?

Diderot says: Premonitions are of no use whatever. It will happen anyway.

Did Hitler know what the fall would bring?

He had a feeling, nothing specific.

Hitler overtaxed

As early as the fall of 1941 the overburdened Hitler declared: "I don't want to hear any more talk about the difficulty of supplying our troops in the winter. There is no need whatever for the least concern about this because there's not going to be any winter campaign. All the Army needs to do is deal the Russians a few powerful blows. Then we'll see what feet of clay the Russian colossus has. I herewith forbid anyone to mention a winter campaign to me." Remarks like this result from overtaxation. Overtaxation resulted from an accumulation of tasks. An accumulation of tasks resulted from lack of confidence. Hitler lacked confidence in the generals. The army is a machine. A machine needs supervision.

Hitler's movements
during the decisive period
from November 19 to 24, 1942

On November 12 Hitler is in Munich. The field staff of the Wehrmacht Command arrives on the 13th at the Munich central railway station by the special train "Atlas"; the Führer's train stops there too. November 14, Salzburg; November 15 to 21, Berghof. November 21, evening, by special train to Leipzig, from there by plane to Wolfsschanze; on the 24th the Wehrmacht Command staff follows him there. November 25 to February 2, Wolfsschanze. Hitler's crucial deliberations up to the 24th took place en route. The change of climate was enough to tire him. Many people cannot think while traveling; they are inhibited by reminders of surprises on arrival, a desire to see the country, the possibility of accidents. Moreover, Hitler talked incessantly to those around him (about millet planting, problems of the Caucasian oil industry, Party measures during 1931; the snow covering the Alps, he said, reminded him of a shroud). After arriving in Wolfsschanze, Zeitzler tried evenings and afternoons to urge him, to persuade him. This activity virtually relieved Hitler of the necessity of decision: his reaction was to turn him down. Furthermore, he lacked confidence in Zeitzler, in his generals, as well as in his own ideas. He was the only member of the extensive array of commanders who lacked confidence in his brain and preferred to rely on his reflexes.

Eye-of-a-needle technique

On November 6, 1942, an agent in the Russian capital reported to the department of foreign armies in the east on a consultation of important military heads in Moscow. Zeitzler mentioned this report on November 9; it produced no reaction. On October 27 Zeitzler expressed the opinion that the flood of enemy propaganda for new major operations was just so much talk. On November 12 Colonel General von Richthofen was already informed of the Russian preparations for an offensive in the Don forests. Both Hitler and Zeitzler considered numerous possibilities: on October 9 Zeitzler regarded a Russian winter offensive as possible; on October 26 Hitler had misgivings about an enemy winter offensive toward an important Black Sea port. Each piece of information had to pass through either Hitler's brain or Zeitzler's; they alone could make decisions. But only one idea at a time could occupy Hitler's and Zeitzler's brains. Hence these two individuals could not properly evaluate either the knowledge of their agents, or that of their colleagues, or their own ideas. The agent who had conveyed the important report of November 6 was apprehended shortly afterward in Moscow and killed.

Hitler

Product of a meager South German Catholic grade-school education. Since their heyday during the Counter-Reformation, these schools have remained underdeveloped.

When he was sure of the nonaggression pact with Russia he banged the wall with his hands and shouted "Victory!" Gushing toward Benito Mussolini over a foreign-political triumph in 1938.

He hops from one leg to the other because of the victory in the west. Blissful when he has betrayed Chamberlain. Like a farmer who has been well represented in court and buys his lawyer a beer, he returns to Munich, goes up the great staircase again to see his foreign minister, gives him a prolonged handshake, sends off another telegram to Benito Mussolini.

Once a decision has been made, there must be new reasons to justify further discussion. No discussion, really, just which way to march!

If there is hope, he can wait for successes. If there is no hope he cannot wait for successes, he rushes into action, drives events forward to rapid disaster.

Because he showed uncertainty toward the generals during Narvik and Dunkirk, he learned that he would have to display confidence in crises; later he could not get rid of the habit.

Colonel General Reinhardt used to make fun of the unprofessional way in which Hitler held his army binoculars. He always maintained: "Hitler can't have seen a thing like that!" After some practice, Hitler was of course bound to see something.

He loved handsome, tall adjutants, young holders of the Knight's Cross. He would touch their necks; they must remain chaste. Many aristocrats did not correspond to this image of the pure aristocracy of which he liked to dream. Good relationship to the women secretaries; he has a valet; he looks well in tails, he is a gentleman, like the one he saw in Linz.

He has become accustomed to the climate of an officers' conference. He often has to laugh when officers really speak the way they do in funny stories; Hitler could imitate that. His mind often wanders.

He rebuked Field Marshal von Kluge: If . . . ; von Kluge hadn't said that at all. What he had said was . . . ; maybe it had sounded like that. But von Kluge was not allowed to correct Hitler; he protested silently. Two weeks later he was in an automobile accident. Hitler: superstitious. Anyone who attacks him in thought comes to grief. Is afraid of snow, weather divide is not weather divide; river, water cause damage, dry land never causes damage; smoking, alcohol, and meat, bad, bad. . . .

Thinks the opposite of the way the man he is talking to thinks. If that man is wrong, Hitler is right. Since Hitler believed that . . . was wrong, he assumed that he, the Führer, had made the right decision. To that extent he relied entirely on . . .'s opinion. He would not listen to any report of disaster unless there was someone to blame. Then he would always define the culprit and the punishment. Chief virtue: making decisions; he would quickly decide against something he didn't want; he quickly wanted something; didn't decide when he wanted two things.

Fond of sweet South German dishes. The most terrible thing of all: pain. By contrast the extinction of existence was not terrible, for that simply meant the end. The self was not worth so much that one could not destroy the self. Very solemn. Sign of fatigue: little jokes in the form of take-offs. Then color would come into his cheeks. His coterie would grin and acclaim him. He could not but laugh at: Franco, von Brauchitsch, Schacht, von Manstein, von Rundstedt, von List, von Kluge, all of whom had hurt him at one time or another.

Train of thought: leaping, clinging stubbornly to one object. Annoyance did not last beyond the next meal but revived at the next reminder. The simplicity of a solution spoke in favor of its correctness. From von Reichenau he heard the phrase or motto: "An operation that is correct in theory need not necessarily be correct in practice." Nearsighted. Hence preferred Jodl's maps

1: 1 million to Zeitzler's maps 1:300,000. He liked looking at charts because facts could be deduced from them. Opinions could be produced by himself, Göring, or Bormann. His doctrine: influence matters so that facts don't become too negative. When he noticed that the secret service used facts to support the General Staff's views, he no longer accepted facts.

Since the occupation of France, Hitler saw practically nothing but headquarters and command posts. Events at the front looked to him like Halder, then like Zeitzler, Schmundt, von Bock, Heusinger. In October and November, 1942, he dispatched six well-known General Staff officers one after another to the threatened front, but naturally they were unable to prevent the collapse. In October placed his hopes in von Seydlitz; in November in Wenck, Speidel, von Richthofen; (secretly) von Manstein, Luftwaffe; in December in von Manstein, Hoth, Raus, Paulus; in January, Field Marshal Milch, General Hube, Paulus up to a point, von Seydlitz very little now; February, again more in von Manstein, the S.S. Panzer Corps. None of these hopes lasted for more than a month.

Ultimate war aims

Germany's task was clearly a Continental one, said Hitler, without prejudicing its claim to a colonial empire, which would embrace Togoland and the Cameroons, including the Belgian Congo. East Africa was desirable but not necessary. War aims for 1942: Hitler told Oshima that Moscow and Leningrad had to be destroyed; we must get to Iran and Iraq, he said, then we can have Afghanistan with us. Japan's main objective must be to take Australia. Ambassador (formerly Vice Chancellor) von Papen, on the other hand, emphasized that this was the right moment to reintroduce the Church in Eastern Europe, whereas Hitler considered the chief problem to be the equipping of the police with tanks and the partitioning of the giant cake so that it could be

1. controlled,
2. administered,
3. exploited.

This meant the threefold task of occupying, introducing order, securing. North Africa must be held at all costs as the forefield of Europe. If Baku and Stalingrad, as well as Saratov, Gorki, Astrakhan, and Archangel could then be secured, everything would be over by October. Possibly the war in Eastern Europe should be dropped.

Hitler was not in the least afraid of England and France, or of the Reichswehr, the Stahlhelm organization, industry, or landowners, since the haves do not fight. He was not fully informed about Russia and America. The Führer was only afraid for his Reich once it joined the haves. That was why he attacked Russia, as long as the prevailing mood permitted.

Napoleon's example

After finally betraying the ideals of the French Revolution, Napoleon invaded Russia. His army comprised 450,000 men. He was opposed by 160,000 Russians. After marching for eighty-four days (including a fourteen-day halt near Vitebsk), he reached Moscow with 95,000 men. On October 19 he began the retreat. Between November 26 and 28 he crossed the Beresina with 14,000 soldiers and 26,000 camp followers. On December 5 Napoleon left Russia. The first ten days of December saw the onset of winter.

Course of action: Napoleon thrust a long arm toward Moscow, then had to withdraw it. Presumably his army did not accompany him voluntarily. In the Europe under Napoleon, 160,000 men had been sentenced in 1810 for refusing to take up arms; reprisals were ordered against their families. In 1811–1812, 60,000 recalcitrants (réfractaires) were sentenced; the winter of 1812 was not an unusually cold one. Napoleon's colleagues later declared Nature to have been hostile to him, so as to camouflage his defeat. But actually there was a flaw in the construction of the campaign. Napoleon's men would have marched to India if anyone had been able to tell them why they should do so.

Hitler did not want to emulate Napoleon!

The generals advised him to advance directly on Moscow. He had no desire to go to Moscow. But if he should end up there, he did not want it to be burned down by the enemy, he wanted to flood it himself!

Hitler's day

Hitler's generals were by tradition early risers. Hitler himself preferred to work at night. He was awakened at 10 A.M. by a servant. Breakfast was brought up to his bedroom by elevator. He then read the foreign newspapers in translation; for this he wore glasses. At 11 A.M. he received Schmundt, decided personnel matters. At noon the situation was reviewed. Lunch began at 2 P.M. and lasted until four; shortly before Stalingrad, Hitler gave up this habit. From then on he ate alone. After lunch Hitler rested until about 6 or 7 P.M. Then he received visitors. Dinner lasted from 8 to 10 P.M. Hitler held forth to a select group until about 4 A.M.

East of Rastenburg, in the Görlitz forest, a hundred yards from a siding of a branch railway, near a country inn, invisible from the road, wooden barracks and concrete boxes (like battleship superstructures in the woods) had been built. Furnishings, dimensions, number of windows, were based on the regulations of the Reich minister of finance for evacuated sections of the Berlin administration. The offices were paneled in light wood covering the concrete walls. Because Hitler was afraid of the sun, the windows faced north.

Hitler and winter

In March, 1942, Hitler was ailing. Hitler had never liked the winter; he had a physical abhorrence of frost and snow. Winter deserved to be cursed, Hitler would say. During events at Voronezh, in the early summer, Hitler remained cool and intelligent. As the summer progressed he became jumpy. He rapidly replaced the commanders under him. At times during this summer, in response to swiftly changing and conflicting orders, four armies would be maneuvering around pockets that did not contain the enemy's major force. Hitler, uneasy, sent two armies to the Caucasus, nearly two armies toward Stalingrad. Strength of will alternated with lack of decision during this summer. The wish to have everything clashed with the fact that in these great spaces there was not much to wish for, unless it were not to have another winter like the last.

Revirement

The idea of having to survive another winter depressed Hitler. He replaced von Bock. He dismissed Chief of General Staff Halder over the question of a retreat. Hitler said: "I demand the same toughness from the command as I do from the front." Halder replied: "I have that toughness, my Führer, but out there brave musketeers are being killed." Hitler replied: "General Halder, how dare you speak to me like that!" Shortly afterward, a quarrel with Field Marshal List, operating in the Caucasus. Hitler sent his assistant, Colonel General Jodl, to List. On the telephone Hitler accused Jodl, who since Narvik had been allowed to sit on his left at table, of letting himself be swayed by List. Jodl was hurt. Hitler planned to replace him as quickly as possible. There was also some ill feeling between Hitler and Field Marshal Keitel. Hitler left his blockhouse by hidden routes only. The conference room was deserted. Hitler no longer took part in the joint meals of the staff. Later Bormann sat in Hitler's empty chair. Within forty-eight hours of the quarrel with Jodl, ten or twelve Reichstag stenographers turned up and from then on took down all military discussions. Göring said: "In the long run it will be to the Führer's disadvantage if everything is taken down." Now the generals spoke only for the record. After von List's dismissal, Hitler was so suspicious that he took over the command of the Caucasus armies himself. After having thus feverishly consolidated all power of command in himself, Hitler left these headquarters and went to Berlin.

Did Hitler have to make the journey?

He did not have to. He needed a change of climate.

Was he uneasy?

First blow

During the night of November 2/3 Rommel gave up in Africa. Hitler assumed there was a conspiracy between Rommel and a fifty-year-old major of Security Ring II who did not have him awakened. On the morning of November 3 Hitler ordered the sallow major, who had a good reputation in civilian life, shot within ten minutes. The major's superior, General Wasilewski, attempted to follow him as far as the steps of Hitler's barracks. He was restrained; the major was transferred to a penal battalion.

Second blow

At noon on November 6 Hitler boarded his official train accompanied by his immediate entourage. The rainy city of Munich would do him good. During the second half of the night the train was stopped at a lonely station in Thuringia and Hitler was informed of the Allied landing in North Africa.

The following day the Führer's train, to all appearances completely empty, stood on a track of the Munich central station among the regular trains. After a search General Wasilewski found General Jodl in the train and could talk to him about the situation. Hitler had a discussion in the "Führer Building" in the Arcisstrasse with the French statesman Laval. Field Marshal Keitel was tossed back and forth between station and Arcisstrasse. The chief of staff of the Supreme Command of the Armed Forces received the incoming bulletins. Later on the special train "Atlas" stood beside the Führer's train.

Third blow

On November 19 the news of Stalingrad; Hitler on the Obersalzberg, the members of Security Ring I with him up there as guests, also Minister Lammers. The rest of the officers in the "Atlas" train near Berchtesgaden; the General Staff in the Masurian forests. Göring's activity: six telephone calls with Kesselring from a hotel in Paris. War plan for the end of 1942? Hit out in all directions! Hitler's quarrel with Jodl prevented the latter from making a further attack on Hitler's self-confidence.

The proposal that the 6th Army should disengage itself came from Colonel General von Richthofen and his Luftwaffe colleagues. Back in East Prussia Hitler saw "excellent prospects" for Stalingrad. On November 29 there was a day-long review of the situation. Hitler said of Field Marshal Rommel in Africa: "You know, I really believe a man should not be left for too long in a position of great responsibility. In time it demoralizes his nerves." Hitler's conviction: all generals are liars, all generals are disloyal, all generals are against National Socialism, all generals are reactionaries.

Hitler's longing: to put on his brown tunic again! To be able to go to the theater and the movies again!

Post-factum localization of responsibility with Hitler. Hitler voluntarily assumed (vis-à-vis Field Marshal von Manstein, whose advice he thereby cut short) the responsibility, i.e., the blame, for the Stalingrad disaster. By doing so he also demonstrated how irrelevant the question of blame was when the disaster had already occurred. Actually responsibility was only of value as an instrument for the prevention of such a disaster. In these dimensions, individual blame scarcely mattered, unless it was to be sought in subordinate positions for purposes of discipline.

VIII
What did the Russians do?

A. Then the Russians attacked on a broad front, the red flag up ahead and bands playing.
Q. Bands playing?
A. Yes, bands playing.
Q. Did you see it for yourselves?
A. Yes, we did.
Q. From what distance?
A. They approached to within 1,000 yards, 800 yards, across the railway embankment.
Q. Can you describe it in a bit more detail?
This is the first time I've heard of it.
It sounds like the days of Frederick the Great.
A. Oh, yes, the ones in the pocket did that quite often.

The Russians put out two pincers, at a sufficient distance from the perimeters of the 6th Army?

On the 19th the northern one, the next day the southern one. The tanks simply drove through.

Who was responsible?

No one really knows. And there's no way of finding out. Things went well.

Did the Russians know what they were doing?

They were attempting an operational measure. Until then they hadn't managed to bring one off.

Which attempts had failed?

The Finland campaign was a disaster. Six times during the winter of 1941 they attempted a pincer movement. The last pincer near Charkov in the spring of '42 was a terrible failure. The Army commander in charge committed suicide. For a long time the comrades wondered whether the exposed flanks to the north and south of Stalingrad were not a German trap.

Might they have been a trap?

Well, the Russians knew there were no more Germans behind the Don. So it wasn't a trap.

So the Russian tanks pushed through?

They pushed through and on the second day (November 21) with both groups, that's to say the north and the south, they made a ninety-degree turn the Germans didn't see. They then advanced on K.; they had this little village and its bridge by noon of the 21st.

Had the Russian commanders believed in a rapid success?

They were amazed. Before that they had already believed in great successes. Without this faith they couldn't have carried out the operation in this way. But in all the previous cases their faith hadn't helped them. Central headquarters in the Russian capital kept phoning the local headquarters of the advancing armies; the comrades asked the reliable comrades Yeremenko and Voronov personally to check the number of prisoners and the places reported captured. They seemed surprisingly favorable.

What did the Russian command think they had surrounded?

They thought possibly 80,000 Germans, a certain number of

Rumanians. The northern and southern arms of the war machine met on November 23 at 4 P.M.; it was just getting dark. Whatever was contained in the Stalingrad area was now surrounded.

Did the Russians notice the counterthrust of the 48th Panzer Corps that was deployed against the Russians' northern group? They noticed nothing.

For two days and two nights the corps, virtually one Panzer regiment, lay immobilized in the midst of the Russian offensive, with weak-sided captured tanks, some of them nibbled by mice. A Rumanian Panzer division belonging to it also lay immobilized a little farther to the northeast. The Russians assumed all this to be a penetrated front, not a counterthrust.

Did they realize the 4th Panzer Army was in the south?

They knew it existed, so they were cautious. All through the late fall Colonel General Hoth, the commander of the 4th Panzer Army, who was high strung, very swift, very decisive, was occupied in shifting one or the other division from his left to his right flank or back to the left, in order somehow or other to form a nucleus. Since early fall he had been stripped; all in all he possessed a bare three divisions and a number of Rumanians. On November 21 he lost his headquarters. The rest of his staff reassembled days later in Nizhniy-Chirskaya. The Rumanian commander C., who until then had been excluded from the Army Command, was to take over the Army; but on that particular day he was not prepared for this. Actually wherever the Russians marched there was nothing. The Russian tanks always detoured wherever they were afraid of difficulties, so they advanced very rapidly.

Did they feel certain of victory?

No, on the contrary, they felt very much threatened. The tank commanders advanced very cautiously and didn't have much time to analyze their successes. They only found out through statements made by prisoners-of-war that they had taken the bridge at K. through an error on the part of the Germans; they thought they had captured it in battle. From above, comrades at headquarters advised caution. The moment of danger was expected to be when the 6th Army marched back onto them, that's to say, back out of the pocket.

What did they do when the 6th Army stayed right where it was?

They harassed in the south and west. In the north they pushed forward when von Seydlitz withdrew slightly. They tried to organize their supply routes and to consolidate the encirclement front. They had no experience in operations of this kind.

Were they especially lucky?

Partly lucky, partly unlucky. They were lucky in the weather on November 19 and 20; Colonel General von Richthofen's pilots couldn't see them. On the other hand, various Russian groups lost their way, but German groups lost their way, too. The capture of the K. bridge was another stroke of luck. A cavalry group rode into a ravine west of the Don and was shot to pieces by the German artillery there. The Russian supply organization functioned poorly until the end of December.

When did they regard the pocket as a *fait accompli?*

When on November 24 there was still no sign of movement in the pocket, when by November 27 the 6th Army had still not broken out. But now they were afraid of Field Marshal von Manstein. They were expecting several relief armies.

Were they informed as to the strength of the Germans?

They possessed numerous sources of information, the German hinterland was after all their own country. They were not well informed.

What did they do when they were certain around November 27 that they had surrounded a pocket with perhaps 80,000 men?

Comrades at headquarters dispatched Colonel General Voronov to the great northern Don bend to organize a second thrust, on the same lines as the northern thrust of November 19. This thrust took place on December 16. It was opposed by Italian forces who gave way immediately.

Was this thrust planned in detail?

No one knows exactly. At first it was a matter of using the same tactics as on November 19. The German or Allied fronts were to be moved farther away from the Stalingrad pocket. Actually Comrade Voronov put an end to Field Marshal von Manstein's southern relief offensive with his thrust. This offensive collapsed because Voronov's thrust from the north threatened the entire hinterland of the Army Group as far as the Black Sea. At this stage Comrade Voronov was already entrusted with new duties.

Did the Russian command regard von Manstein's relief thrust as dangerous?

On December 23 it set up another 400 tanks in readiness south of the pocket area. They did not rely on the thrust in the north.

What did the Russian command do after the termination of the relief thrust?

There were doubts. Colonel General V. was in favor of a respite. Marshal Y. set the 400 tanks to the pursuit of the relief remainder. Voronov and Rokossovski were now to destroy the pocket forthwith. Moreover, the tactics of November 19 were now to be tried out a third time farther north, against the Hungarians. These tactics continued to be the battle plan of the south until the fall of 1944; at Jassy this method again proved successful against the 6th Army. Not until the attack on the Central Army Group early in July, 1944, were new tactics introduced, and these then became standard for Hungary, the battle of the Vistula, and finally for Berlin.

How did the Russians feel after the elimination of the relief forces?

Flags, recorded music, visits exchanged at the front by commanders in chief. It remained to be seen whether the forces surrounded at Stalingrad would break out eastward across the Volga if the river should freeze over; on the other hand, if the Volga were frozen it would be easier for the Russians to organize their own supplies. A few days before the planned major Russian offensive against the pocket in January, 1943, Colonel General Voronov dispatched the following report to comrades at headquarters:

Operation "Ring" by the deadline confirmed by you is not possible because of four- to five-days delay in the arrival of reinforcement units, relief, and ammunition transports. In order to speed up the approach it was necessary to consent to the unloading of many trains and transports at a great distance from the prearranged points. This operation required additional time to bring up unloaded units, relief, and ammunition to the front. Moreover, our correctly calculated plan was crossed up by the inclusion of unscheduled trains and transports for Comrade V.'s left wing. Comrade Rokossovski requests that the deadline be changed by plus 4. All calculations have been checked by me personally. All this compels me to request you to confirm the start of "Ring" with plus 4. I await your instructions. Voronov.

Commander in Chief Comrade Stalin replied: "You will sit there until the Germans capture you and Rokossovski! You have no idea what can be done and what can't be done! We must finish up with all possible speed, and you are deliberately dragging things out!" However, since there was no alternative the deadline was postponed by four days for reasons of caution.

Were the Russians certain of victory now?

They were cautious. In the opinion of the German command of the 6th Army, once the main offensive had begun, i.e., after January 10, they could just as easily have finished off the pocket in four days. They did not make the most of their opportunities because they were afraid of traps. As if according to blueprints, but still without any set pattern, they moved each day one or two miles from west (later also southwest) to east; auxiliary movements came from the north. In the final stage they divided the pocket into first two then three unequal parts, which they split up again. They kept to this method until the end of the war when dealing with pockets.

What did they do when they realized that the pocket contained more than twice as many men as they had suspected?

The officer in charge of Comrade Voronov's enemy information bureau was reprimanded; he should have had no difficulty in obtaining the correct figure on the basis of prisoners' statements. As a result the figure given by Major von K., the fortress quartermaster of the German Army, came as a surprise to the Russian command. Some inadequate preparations for the transfer of such a large number of prisoners were undertaken.

Was victory celebrated on February 2?

Only at a local level, really. Units saluted one another with the obligatory flags. Some of the essential shock troops had already been sent north for a thrust against the Hungarians and the German 2nd Army. On the afternoon of February 2 the High Command left the battlefield by plane. The pocket area came under subordinate command forces. A certain disorganization in this area was attributable among other things to a dwindling away of leaders. On the other hand, the absence of a genuine victory celebration corresponded to the dialectical mode of thought. Operations such as the battle of Stalingrad do not form a victory unit. Actually the Russian campaign begun on November 19 did not come to an end before 1944 with the occupation of Rumania, probably not until the capture of Vienna and Berlin. It is doubtful, however, whether the threat to the Workers' Fatherland was then finally eliminated. There was, therefore, no suitable moment for a victory celebration in the classic style (like Königsgrätz, Sedan, Smolensk, Uman, Briansk, etc.). Of course even the Russians celebrated their victories at some time or other.

IX

Confusion

Ad unum omnes! said school principal Captain (retired) Haul: there are doubts as to whether Caesar had one solitary soldier left to bring him the disastrous tidings, or whether they all, i.e., with not one exception, failed to survive and were found, as it were, where they lay. This cannot be ascertained with certainty from the text. In response to the slogan, "Fight in Stalingrad to the last man and the last cartridge," Major von Z. said: My Führer, the men in Stalingrad can't fight to the last cartridge because they don't have one.

Reconstruction of a battle

FÜHRER: I would like to have a reconstruction. When I leave here I shall probably speak to Antonescu. If I recall correctly, the first report I received stated that two attacks had taken place here, but essentially without artillery or tanks, mainly with infantry, and with no major artillery preparation, and that the Rumanians thought they could manage on their own.

ZEITZLER: That was the first inkling.

FÜHRER: That's how it began: the Rumanians thinking they could manage on their own. Perhaps that partly explains why nothing was done during the first twenty-four hours.

ZEITZLER: For days there were all those messy little actions, and then they didn't really believe anything big was going to develop, and that business down there they also took for a minor attack. That's the real reason. The Russians were quite clever about that, starting off so quietly, giving a false sense of security so that everyone said, it's all minor stuff, and then all of a sudden in that area a big thing blows up. I can prepare a few map sections for you.

Aucun homme n'a reçu de la nature le droit de commander aux autres.

Diderot

About the Author

Alexander Kluge makes his home both in Munich and Berlin. A lawyer by training, he has produced several movies. He won a prize with "Anita G.," a film based on one of the short stories included in *Attendance List for a Funeral,* which McGraw-Hill published in 1966. About it *Saturday Review* noted: "Reading [*Attendance List for a Funeral*] is a sobering experience, and an enlightening one. . . . Kluge creates exemplars of humanity and inhumanity that no reader will ever forget." And *The New York Times Book Review* wrote: "Kluge shows the kind of imagination in his first book that foretells an artist of the first rank."